LIMBO LAND

Published under licence by Brown Dog Books and
The Self-Publishing Partnership Ltd, 10b Greenway Farm, Bath Rd, Wick, nr. Bath BS30 5RL

www.selfpublishingpartnership.co.uk

ISBN printed book: 978-1-83952-474-5
ISBN e-book: 978-1-83952-475-2

Cover design by Kevin Rylands
Internal design by Andrew Easton

Printed and bound in the UK

This book is printed on FSC certified paper

LIMBO LAND

A MEMOIR

KATE BENSON

BROWN
DOG
BOOKS

For Laura and Ray

Sweet is the voice of a sister in the season
of sorrow

Benjamin Disraeli

*Nothing is stronger than a small hope
that doesn't give up*

Matt Haig

CONTENTS

Prologue		11
Chapter 1	Bombshell	13
Chapter 2	Getting There	26
Chapter 3	Devon	42
Chapter 4	Declarations	55
Chapter 5	Hope	65
Chapter 6	Dad	77
Chapter 7	Cycle Three	93
Chapter 8	Onwards And Upwards	104
Chapter 9	Oops!	117
Chapter 10	Homecoming	127
Chapter 11	Time	140
Chapter 12	Home	153
Chapter 13	Ebb And Flow	165

Chapter 14	Bombshell 2	172
Chapter 15	Last Chance	186
Chapter 16	Birthday	199
Chapter 17	Touch And Go	208
Chapter 18	Talk To Me	216
Chapter 19	Back To Devon	225
Chapter 20	The First Few Days	236
Chapter 21	Tick-Tock, Tick-Tock	247
Chapter 22	Over And Out	259
Chapter 23	What Now?	268
Chapter 24	Bye, Bye, Mum	277
Chapter 25	Moving On	287
Epilogue		292

PROLOGUE

2010 was supposed to be a good year, an easy year. A year of recovery and new beginnings. Mum was cancer clear, and I was more than ready to become a mum. 2009 was a blip, a bump in the road; all would come good again in 2010. But as sure as the sun will continue to shine, the shocks and the knocks just keep on coming and my better year, my thank-God-last-year-is-behind-me-year, is turning into my worst year ever!

No. There's still time. There's still hope. It could all still change. Four months of the year remain. The light in my living room shifts and rain drops start to splash onto my window. I can just about make out a robin wagging its tail on the fence outside.

Four.

More.

Months.

CHAPTER 1

BOMBSHELL

The silky, smooth fabric slid over my body like a second skin. A big, bold flower print and a discreet V-neck plunge. Perfect. This kind of shopping experience happens little more than a few times a year and *when* it happens it is to be savoured and enjoyed, like the fall of snow on Christmas Day. There is absolutely no way that anyone else will ever look anywhere near as good in this dress as I do. Fact.

'You okay in there?'

I scrambled for my phone. Five fifteen. Shit! I'd been in this dressing room for over twenty minutes. Ray would be waiting for me.

'Er, fine thanks,' I replied. 'I'll be out in a sec – '

'Okay,' the shop assistant said. 'No hurry.'

I gazed at my reflection one last time. Mum would love it. She would insist I get it. In fact, had she been here, she would probably have marched me out of the cubicle to raid the rails for more of the same. Mum's approach and philosophy to shopping was simple: if it works and you like it buy it, and if it comes in another colour? Well hells bells, buy that too! If shopping were a competitive sport, Mum would be the World and Olympic champion several times over. I, on the other hand, am a lousy shopper. Way too impatient. But what really bums me out about the whole process, and always leads to the mother of all bad moods, is the numerous 'outfit fails' and resulting 'desperate purchase'. You know it's crap. You know it's 'make do', but after several torturous hours undressing and re-dressing you can't go home empty handed.

It is no coincidence that shopping centres are littered with cafes. There is only one known cure to pep up the weary and disgruntled shopper: cake! And not just any old cake – monstrous slabs of it. The greedy and gooey kind of cake that makes you swoon and giggle like a love-struck teen.

Ray! I changed back into my shirt, jeans and trusty brown cowboy boots in record speed and joined the queue to pay. I glanced at my phone. Half an hour late. Bugger. I am *never* late. I am more reliable than the talking clock. I would much rather be half an hour early than a couple of minutes late. Can't help it. It's how I'm wired. I bit my lip. I was annoyed with myself, but then I remembered the reflection in the mirror. Such a beautiful, beautiful …

'That'll be one hundred and sixty pounds please.'

'Sorry?!' I choked.

'One hundred and sixty pounds,' the checkout girl repeated.

Holy cow! I'd been so bloody caught up in the magnificence of the dress and how I looked in it I'd forgotten to check the price tag.

'One hundred and sixty pounds?' I wasn't sure if I was asking, verifying or processing. The girl simply nodded. Okay.

I quickly weighed it up. Did I need it? No. Was it expensive? Yes. Did I want it? Yes. It was a no brainer. I smiled broadly at the girl, slotted my card into the machine and punched in my pin. I would wear it at all four of my next social engagements. And Chris loved it when I showed myself off. Bargain.

'Would you like the receipt in the bag, Ms?'

'Yes please,' I replied.

The checkout girl handed me the bag. 'Have a nice day.'

'Thank you' I gushed. 'You too!' I was grinning like a Cheshire cat. The thrill of the splurge was intoxicating! Mum would most definitely approve.

Now, where the hell was the cinema? I looked frantically around me. This place was huge, the Titanic of shopping centres. Why oh, why, had I not checked the exact location on my laptop this morning? I blew out my cheeks in frustration. The clock on the wall in front of me irritated me further: five thirty-five. Bollocks, bollocks, bollocks – YES! An information stand! I hurried over and quickly located the cinema. Level 4, one floor above the food court. Super. But, according to the map, I was on Level 1 and on the other bloody side of the bloody building! *Not* so super. Oh well. I cursed my bad luck and headed for the escalator.

Ray, my baby-faced younger sister, was sitting on an uncomfortable looking plastic bench underneath one of the film information screens. She was gazing into the distance and biting the inside of her cheek. Her brown shoulder-length hair, which she'd lopped off from waist length to a bob in a fundraiser for mum, was loose and tousled and she was dressed, as usual, in a shapeless black smock and leggings. I've no doubt that on closer inspection I'd find several holes and a frayed hem or two. On her tiny feet – flat, worn-through pixie boots. I shook my head, disbelieving. Five foot five and size four feet. It was a mystery to me how she held herself up. She spotted me and leapt from her seat; arms outstretched in front of her.

'Sorry, sorry – ' I blabbed into a mouthful of her hair as we embraced. 'I tried on a dress, lost track of time – '

'Ooh, let's see, let's see.' Ray's big brown eyes were bulging with excitement.

I opened the bag and let her have a quick peak inside. 'It's lovely,' I cooed. 'I'll show you it properly in a bit.' I closed the bag, smiled, and asked through slightly gritted teeth, 'Been here long?'

'Not really,' she replied. 'I've been here since,' she checked her watch, 'five thirty. Well, actually I've been here since five, but I couldn't find a parking space and I didn't know where the cinema was – '

'– no, me neither. This place is ridiculous!'

'It *really* is...' Ray rocked back onto the heels of her feet, a faint smile forming around the corners of her mouth. 'Gotta be a first I reckon.'

'What has?' I quizzed.

'Me, waiting for *you*!' her eyes glistened with mischief.

'Yes!' I replied, with mock indignation, 'And isn't it annoying?!'
We were both smiling now.

'But technically,' I challenged, 'I wasn't late. I was here *before*
you. If I hadn't got side-tracked by this bloomin' dress I'd have
been here at five and waiting, as usual, for *you*.'

I took a step back, folded my arms and sealed my point with
a matter-of-fact nod of the head.

Ray rolled her eyes. 'Yeah, yeah, whatever – '

'Surrender!' I did a Michael Jackson victory jig. 'You *know*
it, you *know* it.'

'Ah,' sighed Ray. 'Good old MJ.'

We were both Michael Jackson fanatics. Correction, for
a short while in our early to middle teens, we were Michael
Jackson fanatics. We idolised him. While watching him gyrate
and moonwalk in front of us at a show in the late 1990s, Ray
screamed at the top of her lungs. 'I want your babies!' drawing
gasps and giggles from all around us. I was going to be his
backing singer, dancer and co-songwriter and Ray was going
to marry him. His shocking and untimely death the year before
had reignited my love and appreciation of him. For the next
few months, I played his music non-stop and watched YouTube
videos, montages and interviews, 24/7, my obsession well and
truly reawakened.

I was 12 when it all began. The location: Wembley Stadium, the old 'Live Aid' Wembley Stadium. I was with Mum and Ray. Mum had been given tickets to see him by her hairdresser who found herself suddenly unable to go. I'd never heard of him. Which, when I think about it, is a bit odd. Mum is a massive music lover, classical and contemporary, always has been – she possesses a CD collection to rival HMV. Growing up, our home was filled with the sounds of every CD ever released! Favourites, like Annie Lennox, Sting, Genesis and the Bee Gees were played repeatedly and at full whack. I thought I knew everyone and had heard everything. But I hadn't. I was spellbound. Rooted to the spot. Caught up in the wonder of all that what was happening on the stage in front of me. Tears streamed down my face. It was, up until then at least, the most exhilarating experience of my life. Why had I not been alerted to this 'musical genius' sooner? I couldn't believe Mum had kept him from me! I was catatonic! I chastised her immediately after the show. She simply shrugged and explained that she just 'wasn't that fussed about him.' I stood in front of her, mouth ajar, her words ringing in my ears. Blasphemy!

My life was never the same. Two years later there was nothing I didn't know about Michael Jackson. I would challenge my friends to quiz me and would often break out well-rehearsed MJ moves at school discos and sleepovers. But, most significantly, he inspired me. I'd been playing the piano since I was eight years old. I was good and I enjoyed it. Music moved and excited me; I became more and more responsive to it. Songs and poems poured out of me like water gushing from a tap. This was who I was.

Of course, nothing stays the same forever and in 1995 my MJ obsession began to wane. I started going out. Dreams of stadium tours with the King of Pop were slowly being replaced with dreams about boys. Kissing boys. Dating boys. All too suddenly my Michael Jackson fixation seemed childish and out of touch. It *had* to stop. What boy would take me seriously? Almost overnight I banished all my prized MJ possessions from view, stuffing them carelessly into the corner of my wardrobe. Mum walked into my room a few days later.

'Where's your Michael Jackson scarf gone?' she asked, pointing at the top of the window where the absent scarf had hung so proudly.

'Dunno,' came my angsty teenage I-don't-want-to-talk-about-it, reply.

Mum raised an eyebrow; she wasn't going to let this drop. 'Where is it?' she pressed.

'I took it down, okay? No big deal. *Jesus.*' I slammed shut the magazine I was reading in the hope it would put an end to Mum's interrogation.

Mum put her hands up in front of her in mock surrender, 'Okay, okay, just asking.'

I glared at her willing for her to leave. She wouldn't understand.

'If you want to talk about it – ' she began.

'I don't!'

'Okay, fair enough,' she said looking slightly amused. What on earth could be so funny?! 'Dinner's in half an hour or so,' she said. And with that she was gone.

Ray linked her arm through mine. 'The film starts in about forty-five minutes. Let's get some food, I'm starving.'

'Me too,' I agreed. 'What do you fancy?'

Ray thought about it for a bit. 'I'll probably just get a salad.'

I raised my eyes. Surprise, surprise, when *didn't* Ray opt for a salad? Ray jabbed me in the ribs 'Don't be mean.'

'Sorry.' I meant it. It was all too easy to mock her about her eating habits. She couldn't help it. She was gluten intolerant and had been for years. If she ate wheat her face would swell up and her tummy would get all grumbly.

We walked down the stairs to the food court. There was a lot on offer, but I was instantly won over by the unmistakable smell of fish and chips.

'Sold!' I announced. 'I'm having fish and chips.'

There was a salad and juice bar further along. Ray had spotted it too and started heading towards it.

'Shall we sit over there?' she suggested, pointing towards a table and two chairs overlooking the floor below.

'Sure. See you in a bit,' I said heading off to the fish and chip bar.

I tried to wait but Ray was taking so long, and the smell of my food was just too enticing, so I tucked in. Wow, I was hungry! Hardly surprising though, I'd been on the road since midday, and the time was now just gone six.

'Piggy!'

I looked up at Ray from my decimated dinner and held up

my hands in protest. 'Guilty!' I mumbled through a mouth full of fish, '*But!* I continued after a swig of bottled water, 'You'd be just as bad if all you'd eaten today was a crappy chicken sandwich.'

Ray thought about it this for a moment. 'True, true,' she said. And placing her bag under the table, dug her fork into something greenish. 'So, how was the drive down?' she asked.

'Fine,' I replied. 'No traffic and Heart was playing some pretty good tunes so I was singing all the way.' I ate a chip. 'West End Girls came on at one point *and* Tina Turner.'

'Ah,' Ray smiled. 'Mum's faves.'

I scooped up the last remaining piece of fish and lifted it to my mouth. 'I keep hearing songs that remind me of her. It happens pretty much every time I put the radio on.'

We chatted our way through our meal, as we always did.

'Let's see this dress then,' Ray demanded while wiping her mouth with a serviette.

I clapped my hands together excitedly and pulled it from the bag holding it high above my head. 'Like it?'

Ray nodded. 'Very nice,' she said reaching out to touch it.

'Bloody well should be. Cost enough!'

'How much?' she said slumping back in her chair.

I folded the dress up and placed it back in the bag. 'A hundred and sixty quid.'

'Blimey!'

'I know, I know. But it looks amazing on, and I wouldn't be my mother's daughter if I didn't splurge occasionally.'

Ray lowered her eyes slightly. 'I hope she's okay. One of us should be with her.'

I reached out and covered her hand with mine. 'She was in pretty good spirits when I left her at the weekend, and the consultant really seemed to think it'd work this time.' I gave her hand a gentle squeeze.

Ray nodded and wiped a tear from her eye. 'You're right,' she said. 'We have to stay strong; that's why we're here now.'

'The film!' A rush of panic swept through me. 'What's the time?'

Ray glanced at her watch, 'A quarter past six.'

'Bugger,' I shot up out of my seat. 'Film starts in 15 minutes.'

She took a big slurp of her drink.

'Come on!' I pressed.

She took another slurp. She would not be hurried. She would *never* be hurried. 'Okay, okay, keep your knickers on,' she said slowly raising herself up and swinging her bag over her shoulder.

I marched to the bottom of the stairs, looked back but instead of finding her standing behind me I could see she was still at the table fussing with something on her top. I rolled my eyes. Oh, for God's sake! She had no sense of urgency. She was the tortoise, and I was the hare. 'Ray!' I called. '*Come on!*'

She started walking towards me without looking up. Her tardiness was a lifelong bugbear of mine; I had very little patience for it. I tutted loudly as she got closer, making my annoyance audible. Ray ignored me. She simply looked up sweetly, breezed past me and started descending the next set of stairs, taking them two at a time.

'Come on then,' she hollered. 'We don't want to be late ...'

I stared down at her, eyes narrow. Cheeky mare.

'I need the loo,' Ray announced as we arrived at the cinema foyer and was off before I could respond.

We had five minutes before the film was due to begin and the place was rammed. Thankfully, there were no shortage of ticket booths and surprisingly no queues. Woo-hoo! I jumped like a little show pony and trotted towards the nearest one. The total came to fourteen pounds. Yikes! It certainly wasn't cheap to see a film these days; in the 90s it was a mere three quid!

I winced. The noise in the foyer was deafening. Where in the hell had all these people come from? Hurry up Ray! My handbag started vibrating. I could just about hear my mobile's ringtone. Fishing it out of my bag, I glanced at the screen. Unknown. I debated ignoring it. But then raced to a corner of the foyer where I hoped it'd be quieter. 'Hello?' Nothing. I tried again. 'Hello?'

'Hello.' The voice was male and unfamiliar to me. 'Is this Mrs Benson?'

'Yes,' I replied, pressing the phone harder to my ear. 'Who is this?'

'Dr Humphreys, one of the consultants at Derriford Hospital in Plymouth – '

'I'm sorry,' I interrupted, 'I missed that. It's really noisy here. Could you speak up a little please?'

I switched ears.

'Of course,' said the man, slightly louder this time. 'It's Dr Humphreys, one of the consultants at Derriford Hospital in

Plymouth. I am looking after your mum, Sally.' A quick pause. 'Are you okay to talk?'

A chill ran through me. 'Yes.' I wanted to walk towards the escalator, distancing myself further from all the noise, but I was rooted to the spot.

'That's good,' the man's voice had thinned slightly. 'I'm afraid I have some very upsetting news and it won't be easy to hear.'

My eyes went in and out of focus. My heart was beating loud and fast.

'The thing is,' he said clearing his throat, 'your mum hasn't responded to her second course of chemotherapy in the way that we would have liked. In fact, the drugs have had no impact whatsoever.' There was a slow intake of breath. 'And I'm afraid to say, Mrs Benson, there is nothing more we can do.'

The ground below me shifted. I couldn't feel my legs. My head was hot and fuzzy, and the bustle of the foyer had been reduced to a dull drone.

'Mrs Benson?' The consultant's voice sounded a long way off.

I closed my eyes and took a deep breath. 'What do you mean?' I stuttered.

'Like I said,' he replied. 'There's nothing more we can do. We've done all we can. I'm very, very sorry.'

My throat tightened and I could feel tears pricking the back of my eyes. 'But, but that doesn't make any sense!' Anger was rising from the pit of my stomach. 'We were told she would receive intensive treatment for six months, and if a cycle didn't work you would simply select a different cocktail of drugs and try again.' I clutched at my chest fearing my thumping heart would burst at any second. 'She's only been in hospital for five weeks and this was only her second cycle.' My eyes were awash with tears.

There was a heavy sigh. 'I'm afraid it's a little more complicated than that, every case is different. Your mum's cancer is very aggressive. We've tried two cycles, the second consisting of the strongest drugs available. We've simply run out of options.'

I blinked away my tears and steeled myself for an answer to a question I had no choice but to ask. I took my time. 'So,' I swallowed hard. 'She's going to die?'

Ray's smiling face sprung into view.

'Yes,' he said. 'I'm afraid she is.'

CHAPTER 2

GETTING THERE

I gripped the railing, convinced I was about to fall. In a matter of minutes my world had been turned completely upside down.

'How long?' I asked.

The reply was quick and flat.

'Weeks.'

I'd stopped breathing. Ray was standing just a few feet away, her eyes locked on mine, her brow scrunched with concern. I slowly shook my head, tears rolling down my face. *Weeks.*

'How is she?' I croaked.

Ray took a wary step back.

'Devastated, as you'd expect. She's being comforted by one of the nurses.'

She was all alone. We'd left her all alone. She was in that pokey, windowless room, all on her own. What on earth must she be thinking?! How would she be feeling? My heart ached to see her. I stood up straight and wiped the tears from my face. 'We're on our way.'

'Okay,' the consultant said in a tone that was impossible to read. 'I look forward to seeing you.' Adding, 'I truly am very, very sorry.'

'Thank you,' I managed a tight smile. 'Goodbye, Dr Humphreys.'

I stared at Ray's scared eyes for what seemed like forever. I couldn't say it and she couldn't ask.

'Mum's cycle hasn't worked,' I said finally, barely recognising the sound of my own voice. 'The consultant says she can't have any more treatment and,' Ray's eyes were filling up and her lower lip was trembling 'and ...' I couldn't say it, not out loud. I broke Ray's gaze and stared up at the ceiling. Bloody hell! I closed my eyes and took several deep breaths.

'Gus?' Ray's little voice and the use of my nickname pierced my heart. What I was about to say would destroy her. I pulled myself together and forced myself to look at her.

'She's not going to make it, Ray. They've done all they can. The consultant reckons she has only weeks left to live.'

Neither of us moved. We were frozen in the moment; this horrific, ridiculous moment. My mum was going to die. I could feel my legs starting to wobble again when Ray broke the silence.

'I don't get it,' she said running her hands through her hair. 'They said she'd be in hospital for six months. Surely they can just – '

'Try something else?'

Ray nodded.

'That's what I said but according to Dr Humphreys it isn't that clear-cut. Mum's cancer is aggressive, and he says the drugs just aren't touching it.'

'So they give up?' the colour had returned to Ray's cheeks.

That's what it seemed like. Mum's heart-shaped face filled my head. We had to see her. We had to be with her. Ray and I looked at each other for a couple of seconds.

'Hug?' Ray suggested.

We wrapped our arms around each other, fresh tears filling my eyes. Everything was cloudy, nothing made any sense. This wasn't my life. I'd fallen asleep watching the film and was dreaming. I'd wake up in a minute and everything would be the way it was.

Laura. I untangled myself from Ray's embrace and flipped open my phone scrolling through my contacts until I'd reached my big sister's name and number. I clocked the time. Damn, she'd probably be bathing the boys. Should I wait? No, this couldn't wait.

'Laura?' Ray guessed.

I nodded and pressed the dial button. Laura's husband Mark answered on the third ring.

'Hello?'

'Oh, hi Mark, it's Kate. Is Laura there?'

Ray gave me a little smile, urging me on.

'She is, but she's upstairs with the boys – '

'Can you get her please?' I interrupted. 'It's really important.'

'Sure, hold up.' Mark bellowed up the stairs, 'Laura! It's Kate.'

One of the boys was being reprimanded for hogging a toy.

'Jacob's clean, so is Nathaniel,' I heard her tell Mark. 'Sebastian isn't.' A few seconds later Laura was on the line.

'Hey, sorry about that. You okay?'

No and neither will you be. I rolled my shoulders and began the inevitable.

'Mum's consultant just called. The cycle hasn't worked,' I began. Ray reached out and held my hand. 'He says they've done all they can and it's now just a matter of time.'

Silence.

'Who did you speak to?' Laura asked eventually, her voice tight but controlled.

'Dr Humphreys,' I replied.

'What else did he say?'

'That was it really.' Or was it? Everything suddenly seemed very unclear.

'*Why* didn't it work?' Laura prompted.

'He didn't say.' Or did he? My memory was fuzzy. 'He said something about running out of options, and that mum's cancer was aggressive – '

'Well, we know that,' Laura barked. 'That's why she was rushed into hospital in the first place! Why not try a different cocktail? That's what they said they'd do.'

'They can't.' My body sagged with sadness and defeat.

'They can't?!' Laura's fear and frustration was palpable. 'Why not?!'

Dr Humphreys, I could hear him now, clear as a bell 'because' I began, 'they've already used all the drugs available and there are no other drugs to try.'

Another silence.

I slumped against the wall behind me, utterly deflated.

'So, what now?' Laura's tone had softened. 'Have you told Ray?'

I sighed a long, heavy sigh. 'Yes, she's with me now. We're at Westfield. We were about to watch a film when I got the call.'

'Oh yeah, I forgot about that, sorry.'

Mark was shouting at one of the boys. 'No, *now* Nathaniel, I've asked you *three* times!' I could hear Laura walking away from the commotion, down the stairs and into the kitchen. 'Are you going to drive down to Devon tonight?'

'I think so,' I replied. 'I haven't spoken to Ray about it yet. I wanted to speak to you first, but yeah, probably. I hate that she's all alone.'

'Me too.'

'What about you?'

Laura would probably drive to and from Devon on the very same day. Last week and the week before she'd arranged for someone to look after the kids, set off for the three-hour drive to Devon at dawn, arrived at the hospital by eight and left by one so she could be home by four/five to cook dinner for her boys. It was crazy, but it was the only way she could be in two places at once.

'The usual, probably. I'll obviously need to check with Mark first, but I can't *not* be with her,' she said.

I nodded. 'Are you going to call her?'

I wasn't sure I could talk to Mum right now, though I desperately wanted to. 'I might just text, tell her we're on our way, that I love her and that I'll see her in the morning.'

'Hmmm,' Laura mulled it over. 'I'm not sure.'

Mark was still yelling at Nathaniel. 'I'd better go. Safe drive, yeah. I'll see you in the morning – '

'Wait!' I cried. 'What about Dad? Should we tell him?'

Dad wasn't exactly flavour of the month with any of us at

the moment. We were all a bit upset with his behaviour over Christmas and as a result none of us were really speaking to him. Laura was always the voice of reason. 'Let's wait till we get down there, till we've spoken to the consultants, properly.'

'Good plan.'

Nathaniel was screaming the house down. 'Gotta go,' Laura hurried. 'See you tomorrow. Love you.'

'Love you,' I echoed, but she was gone before I'd even begun.

It was nearly seven. The cinema foyer had emptied, and Ray and I were alone. My head was throbbing.

'I need to sit down,' I said, rubbing my temples.

We walked slowly and deliberately to a bench just a few feet away and sat and stared into the distance, like a couple of zombies. Mum was going to die. Mum, the woman who brought me into this world and loved me and knew me like no other, would soon no longer be in it. Seriously?! I scrunched up my eyes in disbelief, shook my head and let out a little laugh.

'This is bollocks!' I said. 'Mum can't die!' I swivelled round to look at Ray who was staring back at me.

'I know,' Ray replied. 'It's just, so – '

'Ridiculous?' I suggested.

'Yeah,' agreed Ray. 'Ridiculous. Totally and utterly ridiculous.'

I nodded and settled back into the bench, relieved to have come to some sort of shared, coherent understanding. A rush of hope rippled through me 'We need to get to Devon.'

'Agreed,' replied Ray, biting the skin around her thumbnail.

I lightly slapped her hand away. 'Mum doesn't like it when you do that.'

Ray looked shocked then sad and slowly crossed her arms.

A couple of seconds later I'd concocted a plan.

'How about I drive us both down to Devon from mine? We can stop off at yours on the way so you can pick up a few bits and ditch your car.'

It sounded like a good plan to me. Ray didn't look so sure.

'I'm thinking we might need both cars when we're down there,' she ventured. 'You never know.'

She had a point. Something might crop up or one of us might need to leave. We didn't want to be trapped. I put my arm around her and pulled her towards me giving her a good squish. 'Good plan, Batman.'

Ray smiled and rested her head on my shoulder and for a few, precious minutes, the panic and pain subsided.

An hour and a bit later we had arrived at Ray's flat in Clapham. I wasn't sure at first whether or not to go in. Christian, Ray's boyfriend, would be there and I didn't want to intrude. Also, I wasn't sure I could face him. He'd try and comfort me and I wasn't ready. Too late. He'd spotted me and was beckoning me in from the doorway. I grabbed my coat, stepped out of my car, and headed towards his outstretched arms. I quickly wriggled free; his hug felt all wrong. There was only one pair of arms that I wanted, and they were over sixty miles away in Oxford.

Christian was holding a box of assorted chocolates and was waving them under my nose.

'Want one?' he offered.

'She doesn't eat chocolate, Christian.' Ray emerged from the kitchen clutching a bottle of water. 'How many times?!'

Christian popped another one into his mouth. 'Sorry.'

I waved my hands in front of my face. 'Don't worry about it,' I reassured him. 'Nobody ever remembers. Dad still buys me Easter eggs.'

Ray rolled her eyes. 'Right, better get packing,' she said taking a swig of water. 'Help yourself to anything in the kitchen, Gus, I'll be as quick as I can.'

Christian and I were left standing awkwardly in the hallway. 'Why don't you go and help her?' I suggested. 'I'll wait in the lounge.'

Christian nodded and bounced off after Ray like Tigger. It made me smile. His childlike vibe was irresistible. He was a big, warm-hearted guy, full of boundless energy and verve. His world, as far as I could tell, revolved around two things: food and fitness. He walked around with his nose permanently stuck in the air, sniffing out and following smells, like a cartoon character.

I made my way to the lounge and lowered myself into a cold and uninviting black leather sofa. I slowly took in the room, until my gaze fell upon a small black and white photograph on a shelf above the TV. A swirl of fear started to stir in the pit of my stomach. I slowly rose from the chair and tentatively walked towards it. It was a photo of all of us – Mum, Dad, Laura, me and Ray. We were all smiling and holding cocktails. I zoned in on Mum. Her brown/gold curly hair sat neatly on her shoulders. My chest and throat tightened. The photo was probably five or six years old. I balled my hands into fists and closed my eyes blinking away a solitary tear. What was happening? Where was I? I couldn't think straight. I stumbled into the kitchen and gulped down a glass of water. Slamming the empty glass on the kitchen worktop, I took a couple of deep breaths. Everything is going to be okay, I told myself. Everything will work out just fine.

It was dark by the time we got to Oxford. I pulled into my usual parking space, quickly got out of my car and motioned for Ray to park in the space behind me. It wasn't our designated spot, but at this hour no one would complain. I leaned back against the passenger door of my Toyota and looked up at the sky. It was a clear, starry night. One star was bigger and brighter than the others. Venus? That was the planet you were supposed to be able to see with the naked eye, right?

'I don't need to bring my stuff in, do I?'

I turned my head in Ray's direction who was peering up at me through the open window of her car.

'No,' I replied. 'We'll be heading off as soon as I'm packed.'

A few seconds later we were walking up an unlit path towards an ugly sixties style block of flats. I hadn't wanted to rent the flat at first. The area was a little unsavoury and a stark contrast to the sweet little house we'd rented previously. But, as nice as that house was, it was too small. Chris and I had accumulated a lot of stuff over the years, and we desperately needed more space. This flat was bigger and because it was owned by a mate of Chris', was considerably cheaper. So, despite my misgivings about the building and the area, we moved in.

As I started the ascent up the communal stairs to the second floor, a familiar ripple of excitement swept through me. I smiled and shook my head in disbelief. How was it still possible to get a little giddy at the thought of seeing my husband? Wasn't this sort of thing supposed to wear off? We weren't love struck teenagers or newly-weds – we were both thirty-one and had been together for over ten years!

I inserted a key into the lock of my front door and purposefully walked into the flat. I could hear plates clattering above the babble of the TV. I eagerly followed the noise through the lounge and stopped in the doorway of the kitchen.

'Hey,' I said.

Chris spun round and putting down the plates he was holding quickly closed the gap between us. With one long step, he drew me into an embrace. Home. I collapsed into him and cried like a baby.

'She's going to die!' I wailed, over and over, as Chris rocked and soothed me. It was all so suddenly and terrifyingly real. Chris tightened his grip and kissed the top of my head. The outbursts eventually stopped, and my tears slowed. My nose was stuffed with snot, and I couldn't breathe. I jerked my head up from Chris' chest so I could inhale through my mouth. He looked down at me intently. 'I'll get you a tissue,' he said and disappeared from the kitchen.

I turned round and came face to face with Ray who was sitting on the edge of the sofa, eyes filled with tears. She was still wearing her coat and boots. Chris returned with a fistful of toilet roll. I took the wad and tried and failed to blow my nose.

'Okay?' Chris asked. And reaching out he tucked a stray lock of dyed-blonde hair behind my ear. I nodded. Although I felt as far away from okay as the stars were from earth. I smiled at Ray who had nestled back into the corner of the sofa.

'Sorry,' I began. 'I don't know what came over me.'

'Don't be silly,' she said. 'What are you sorry for?'

'For being hysterical,' I replied.

'If you're going to be sorry about anything, be sorry about the state of your face!'

I looked at Chris who was supressing a smirk.

'Pretty scary,' he admitted.

Ray started giggling. 'You've got a bright red nose and mascara *everywhere!*'

I walked over to Ray and wiped my snotty, messy face all over hers.

'Urgh!!' she shrieked through giggles as she struggled to push me away. 'Yuck! Stop it! Chris – get her off me!'

'No chance,' he said. 'You're on your own.'

I slumped onto the sofa beside Ray and sighed. 'This is all so fucked up.'

'Certainly is,' Ray agreed, kicking off her boots and curling her legs up underneath her. 'And we've still got to get to Devon.'

I grimaced and stretched my arms high above my head. 'It's going to be a long, hard drive, but we might as well get moving.'

'You're going tonight?!' Chris was perched on the arm of the sofa next to me, his hand rested on my thigh.

'Yep – '

'I don't think that's a good idea,' he interrupted 'You're in no state to drive all that way. Go in the morning.'

I shot up and marched into the kitchen. Try as he might, Chris was not going to change my mind.

'No, no,' I began. 'We're going as soon as I've packed.' I reached up into the cupboard next to the sink and grabbed a glass. 'We want to get to Devon overnight so that we can see Mum first thing tomorrow morning.' I turned the tap on and let the water run.

'I really don't think that's a good idea.'

I held up my hand to silence him. Testing the temperature of the water, I filled my glass. 'We're going tonight. We *want* to go tonight.'

I stared into Chris' slate blue eyes and gulped down the entire contents of my glass. Chris didn't say anything.

'It's for the best,' I reassured him.

Chris simply shrugged, defeated. 'Okay, fine, whatever you want.'

I stretched up onto my tiptoes and kissed him on the cheek. He softened and smoothed a thumb across my mascara-stained cheek.

'You really do look ridiculous,' he smiled.

I reached up and grabbed his hand. 'You *are* ridiculous.'

We looked at each other for a little while and hugged it out. I breathed him in. Here in these arms everything made sense; no harm or pain could come to me. I wondered how long it would be before I saw him again; before I would feel safe again. My throat tightened. I pushed the thoughts away. I couldn't think about this now. I gave Chris a squeeze and released him. I needed to pack. I removed my coat, draped it over the back of the sofa and headed for the bedroom.

I packed with speed and little thought. We had no idea how long we'd be in Devon, but we did know we'd be at either Mum's house or the hospital. I didn't need heels or party dresses, but I did need warmth and comfort. Underwear, obviously, plus several pairs of boots and flats. I'd have got the job done a whole lot quicker had Chris not insisted I eat something. I really wasn't hungry and resisted all his initial offerings but having dug my heels in about travelling overnight and not in the morning I relented and found myself agreeing to beans on toast. Ray, who, unlike me, had somehow managed to convince Chris that she didn't need any food, found my initial reluctance, and the whole exchange, hilarious. Just before we left though, I got my revenge. Desperate for the loo, as she always was, Ray jumped off the bed a little too eagerly and landed straight onto my discarded plate. She slipped and fell. Now *that* was funny.

Ray and I drove to Devon in convoy. Each of us alone with our thoughts for almost four hours. The motorways were eerily quiet, and every now and again, lost in thought and fighting off sleep, I'd catch myself drifting between lanes. I didn't switch on the radio – there was a loud enough babble inside my head. Three hours into the journey and it all got a bit too much. I was exhausted. I indicated left and pulled up onto the hard shoulder, just a few miles from the Exeter turn-off. Ray duly followed and rolled to a stop behind me. It was such a relief to turn off the engine, pull up the handbrake and release my grip on the steering wheel. I stretched my feet and rolled my shoulders. I could have fallen asleep forever. Ray was out of her car and peering through my window with a quizzical look on her face. She was huddled over and shivering. I motioned for her to go round to the passenger door and get in.

'What's up?' she asked.

'I just had to stop,' I replied, stifling a yawn. 'I couldn't keep my eyes open a moment longer. I kept drifting from lane to lane.'

'I know,' said Ray. 'I saw.'

'I was worried I'd crash if I didn't pull over.'

Ray nodded and rubbed her eyes. 'I've been yawning my head off. Could really do with a power nap.'

A power nap was exactly what we needed. We were only about an hour away from Mum's, so we had time.

'Probably best we stop off properly at the Exeter services,' I suggested. 'We can kip in our cars for bit, get something to eat and drink – '

'Go to the toilet ...'

I smiled. 'Go to the toilet and be on our way.'

The power nap was a disaster. Sleep for me was almost impossible anywhere other than my own bed, and my body and brain couldn't be fooled and refused to shut down. Ray, on the other hand, was sound asleep. She looked so still and peaceful. I turned away, took a couple of deep breaths, reclined my chair a little further and closed my eyes. I was back at War Coppice, my beloved childhood home. I was curled up on the sofa watching a film with Mum, Dad, Laura and Ray. We were all engrossed in the film. Well, all of us accept Mum. She'd fallen asleep. This wasn't unheard of, she often dozed off and it amused us all greatly. Her head, as usual, was lolloped to one side, her mouth ajar. Every now and again her mouth would close, and her head would jerk upright before slowly slipping back. We'd all signal each other and start giggling. Dad would pause the film and shout, 'Love – wake up!' Startled, Mum would sit up with a confused look on her face, see us all smiling at her and say, 'What?!' without fail. Laughter would ripple around the lounge.

'You were asleep,' one of us would say.

'Rubbish!' would come Mum's reply as she wiped spittle from the corner of her mouth. 'I was just resting my eyes.'

More laughter.

'You were totally out it!' we'd all rejoice in telling her. Mum would shake her head, adamant she'd just dozed off for a bit. She needed convincing.

'You were!' we'd insist. 'You were catching flies.'

'Was I?' And then she'd come over all sheepish, a little grin appearing. 'Oops. Well, I'm awake now. What have I missed?'

'Half the film,' one of us would reply.

'Oh, pischt, now you're just being ridiculous.' And she would rearrange herself in her chair and look towards the TV with an eager look in her eyes. 'Come on,' she'd say. 'Rewind it.'

'No!' We'd cry in unison.

She'd missed way too much and even if we did rewind the film, we all knew she'd be asleep again minutes after Dad pressed play.

'Well, is it any wonder I never know what's going on?'

'Ready?' Dad would ask, looking at all three of us.

We'd nod in reply and the film would resume. About ten minutes would pass and, once again, Mum's head would be lolloping back and forth.

CHAPTER 3

DEVON

Mum's sugar-cube cottage sprung into view and my heart sank. It was meant to be the house she'd grow old in. She'd fled here just over three years ago in a brave bid to start again. Initially, although struggling with loneliness, all was well. It had been a turbulent few years, and the three-bed cottage which sat in a remote location just a few miles from Tavistock, provided Mum with the peace and space she'd craved. But, it wasn't to last. Just six months after moving, she was diagnosed with breast cancer. She was fifty-six years of age.

The beep of a car horn startled me. I glanced up at my rear view mirror. Ray was looking at me with a puzzled expression. She was probably wondering why I'd stopped. I lowered my window and signalled for her to park in front of the garage. I carried on to the gate at the far end of Mum's garden and parked in the tricky spot by the pond. Ray, I knew, would be grateful. She'd backed into the narrow gate on her first visit to the house and was more than a little reluctant to try again.

I met her at the back door, which Mum had had painted pillar box red the month before last.

'Thanks for parking at the back,' Ray said. 'I really must stop being such a wuss about it.'

'No probs,' I reassured her. 'Got the key?'

A couple of seconds later we were in. It was cold and a little musty, as the property hadn't been lived in for a while, apart from when Mum and I stayed a couple of weeks ago, a twenty-four-hour reprieve from hospital between cycles. Ray dumped her bags on the kitchen surface and let out a hippo-size yawn.

'What time is it?' she asked, stretching her neck from side to side.

I retrieved my mobile from my handbag, 'A little after five.'

'I think I need a bit more sleep,' Ray mumbled, 'I'm totally whacked.'

'We can't see Mum till eight, so we might as well,' I agreed.

Just at that moment Wilf, Mum's beast of a dog, came bounding into the kitchen crashing into the chair by the coal fire and then into Ray, almost knocking her off her feet.

'Wilfy!' Ray cooed, wrapping her arms around his neck, and kissing the top of his head, 'So good to see you!'

Wilf's tail was wagging at supersonic speed, his long bony legs bent and quivering with excitement. I feared he might wee and neither of us needed to deal with *that* right now. His sister, Darcy, would be about somewhere, curled up on the sofa, no doubt. Darcy wasn't really a dog – she trotted about with an air of distain and nonchalance; she'd never lower herself to typical dog-like displays of love and devotion – she was above all of that. There would be no enthusiastic greeting; we probably wouldn't see her until dinner time.

'I'm going upstairs,' I told Ray, who was still fussing over Wilf.

'Okay,' she replied. 'Be up in a sec.'

I squeezed past her, patted Wilf hello and made my way to the larger of the two spare bedrooms. Mum's room was the first on the left. I had a quick peek inside. The duvet was rolled back, as it always was when Mum wasn't in the bed and clothes were hung up all around the room. I took a deep breath in – Chanel No 5 – the smell of the room made me smile.

'Do you think she'll need anything?' Ray had more or less followed me up the stairs and was standing behind me, peering over my shoulder and into Mum's room.

'No,' I replied. 'She's got two clean pairs of pyjamas at the hospital. I washed and ironed them last time I was here and dropped them off before I left.'

My eyes were stinging with strain and exhaustion and my head was pounding. I stumbled into the bedroom and fished out a couple of paracetamols from my handbag. I washed them down and flopped onto the double bed. Surely I'd be able to nod off this time? I picked up my mobile and set an alarm. I'd only need an hour.

'Ah Gus, Gus,' Ray was standing in the doorway wrestling with her big, chunky jumper. 'You look so cute!'

I half opened one eye and raised a disbelieving eyebrow.

'You do, you do!' Ray insisted and jumped into the bed alongside me.

I clutched at the duvet and snuggled in as tight as I could. 'Night, night, Ray,' I whispered and drifted into darkness …

It took me forever to find a parking space Some days it was super busy, other days you'd have no problem at all. My mobile was ringing. It was Laura. I handed Ray some change for the parking meter.

'Hey,' I answered. 'You okay?'

'So, so,' replied Laura. 'A bit freaked out actually.'

'Oh?' I fiddled with the zip on my coat. 'What's up?'

There was a slight pause before she continued, 'It's Mum, she doesn't appear to be upset at all.'

Laura had been with Mum just over half an hour; she'd arrived at the hospital at eight.

'Really?' I replied, bemused.

'I know – it's really weird, she's chatting away like normal, as if everything is okay.'

That *was* strange.

'Denial?' I ventured.

'Don't think so – she *has* mentioned it, but mostly she's smiling away and chatting about anything and everything else. Thought I should warn you cos it's a little unsettling.'

'Okay.' To be honest nothing about this situation made any sense to me anyway so why should Mum's response? 'We've just parked, be up in a bit.'

I switched off my phone and breathed in long and hard. This was going to be a difficult day.

'Laura says Mum's pretty chipper,' I told Ray as we passed

.ough the entrance doors to the hospital and made our way towards the lifts at the far end of the building. Ray raised both eyebrows in surprise. 'I know. It's freaking Laura out a bit.'

We dismissed the lifts for the stairs. The more time you spend in hospital the more ill-health you see and it makes you incredibly grateful. We always took the stairs and climbed them without complaint. We left the stairs at level 3 and followed the signs for haematology.

Our pace quickened as we neared Mum's ward. So close! We were in such a hurry that we almost forgot to stop at the soap dispenser at the entrance of the ward. I clocked Mum's name 'Sally Jones' on a big white board of patient information. I turned right towards a block of five bays. Mum was in the first one on the left. I turned the corner, Ray trailing behind me, and stopped briefly as soon as I saw Laura. She was sat cross-legged on a chair at the end of Mum's bed. Her long brown hair was scraped back into a high ponytail and her face was bare. She looked up at me with big, blue, weary eyes and smiled warmly. I dropped my handbag at the side of a little white cabinet to the left of where Laura was sitting.

'Hello,' Laura was on her feet and hugging me. It was a long and loving hug. I hadn't seen my big sister since before Mum was taken ill. We always visited separately due to work and childcare. I turned to face Mum. She was looking straight at me. There was a pain in my chest I had never experienced before. It felt as if someone was squeezing my heart. We smiled at each other.

'Hey you,' I said walking towards her.

'Morning Kate-kins.'

I bent down to kiss the top of her round, hairless head. Nobody rocked the bald look like Mum; Yul Brynner being a notable exception. I lowered myself onto the plastic chair by her bedside, took her hand and drank her in. My mum was beautiful, even bald and cancer ridden. She had a glow and a sparkle that shone from within. The glow was, in part, due to her enviable perma-tan. She'd spent quite a bit of time in her garden before being admitted to hospital and her tan was sticking. It always did. I hadn't inherited her olive complexion. I, annoyingly, was fair, like my dad. I *do* tan, but it takes a while and sunbathing isn't really my thing – a bout of severe sunstroke on a family holiday to Turkey when I was fourteen had put a stop to that. I sit in the sun, but not for long stretches of time or without a generous caking of factor twenty.

Ray had sat herself on the other side of the bed and like me was staring at Mum intently.

'How you doing?' she asked.

Mum shrugged her shoulders, 'Okay, not much I can do about it really, is there?'

Ray glanced over at me and then back at Mum. 'Suppose not,' she replied.

At that moment a nurse walked into the room. I didn't recognise her. She was plump with a mousey bob and looked to be about twenty-five. She bent down and picked up a chart at the end of the bed.

'Morning Sally,' she said, removing a pen from her top pocket. 'My name's Sarah, I'll be looking after you this morning.'

Mum looked at her and nodded.

'I just need to ask you a few questions, is that okay?'

'Do I have a choice?'

I covered my mouth to hide my smile. Sarah took us all in then rested her gaze on Mum.

'No, not really,' she admitted with a flash of a smile.

Sarah wasn't amused. She had a job to do. She looked down at the chart.

'When did you last eat, Sally?'

'About half an hour ago,' Mum replied. 'I had a banana.'

Sarah scribbled something on her sheet.

'Okay, and what about your fluids? What have you had to drink this morning?'

Mum looked over at her bedside table.

'A cup of Earl Grey and an orange juice.'

Sarah frowned.

'That's it? No water?'

Mum shook her head and made a face.

'No, it's not very nice.'

Sarah scribbled something else onto the chart and put her pen back in her pocket.

'I'll get you a fresh jug. You really should try and drink a bit more.'

She put the chart back in the slot at the base of Mum's bed. 'I'll be back within the hour to do your obs. The doctors start their rounds at eleven so you'll be seen before midday.'

'Excuse me,' Laura was looking at Sarah with a sweet but stern expression. 'Is there any chance the doctors could come and see us any sooner?'

We all stared at Sarah who looked a little thrown.

'I don't – '

'It's just that we'd like to get to the bottom of what's happening,' Laura continued. 'They've decided to stop my mum's treatment and we'd like an explanation. Could they perhaps drop in here first?'

It was unlikely. The doctors always started their rounds at the other end of the ward, and by the look on Sarah's face today would be no different.

'I can ask,' Sarah replied. 'But I wouldn't get your hopes up.'

Laura, never one to give up, continued to stare up at the nurse, a tight smile fixed to her face.

'Good,' she barked, 'ask.'

And there it was, the 'don't-mess-with-me-you-will-do-as-I-say' direct tone that made all who heard it, including grown men, tremble in fear.

'Y-yes,' Sarah stuttered. 'Of course, right away.'

Poor Sarah; I attempted to soften the blow. 'That'd be great,' I began. 'Thank you very much. We'd all really, *really* appreciate it.'

Sarah nodded and quickly backed out of the room. I shook my head teasingly at Laura.

'What?!' she exclaimed, all wide eyes and innocence.

'You *know* what!' I challenged; a big smile plastered on my face.

Laura folded her arms, smiled and shrugged.

'Silly woman.'

This made me laugh. Laura had no time for nonsense, if she wanted to know something or get somewhere there was absolutely no stopping her, and woe betide anyone who got in her way or failed to do as she asked. I, along with the rest of my family, found her stern and direct tone amusing, and, knowing it was harmless, paid little attention to it. But for those who were unaccustomed to it or were experiencing it for the first time, it was unexpected and it stung *hard*. Laura was aware of it, but adopted a 'laissez-faire' attitude about it; this is how I operate, no bells, no drama.

'How are the dogs?' Mum asked, wiping the lenses of her bright red glasses with a cloth.

'Fine,' I replied, 'Well, actually, I didn't see little Miss Snooty Pants – surprise, surprise, but I'm sure she's fine.'

Mum shot me a 'don't-be-mean' look.

'She's just – '

'Aloof,' I interrupted. 'I know, so you always say, but that's just a diplomatic way of saying she's stuck up and couldn't care less. Crap dog.'

Mum laughed.

'You've never liked her, poor thing.'

'What's to like?!' I shot back in defence. 'She's cold and completely and utterly unlovable.'

Mum's mouth dropped wide open in disbelief – you'd think I'd just admitted to murdering my neighbour. Laura and Ray were giggling.

'Well,' Mum said while putting her glasses back on, doubling the size of her already big, brown eyes. 'Ray likes her, don't you Ray?'

'Yeah,' nodded Ray, unconvincingly. 'She's alright.'

Mum playfully struck the back of her hand.

'Well,' she concluded, pausing briefly to look at us all, one by one, '*I* love her and that's all that matters.'

We looked up at the sound of a gentle knock. One of Mum's consultants, Dr Clarke, was standing in the doorway, a little hunched. I'd only met him once. There were six haematologists altogether, some we saw more than others.

'Hello.' Dr Clarke stepped into the room. He was a tall, slender man with greying hair. I felt a familiar surge of fear sweep through me.

'Sorry for the interruption,' Dr Clarke said. 'One of the nurses asked if I could pop in and see you. Is everything okay?'

Laura was the first to speak.

'Hi, um, no, not really.' She sat up a little taller in her chair and reached out her hand for Dr Clarke to shake. 'I'm Laura, one of Sally's daughters, we haven't met.'

Dr Clarke shook her hand.

'Dr Clarke, nice to meet you.'

Laura nodded.

'We'd like some clarification on Mum's condition, please. We're all a bit confused. Why is her treatment being stopped?'

Dr Clarke clasped his hands together and slowly raised them to his chin. It was a while before he spoke. 'Leukaemia is a very complicated disease and Sally's leukaemia is very aggressive. More aggressive than we first anticipated. When a patient first presents with the disease we begin a standard in-house course of chemotherapy straight away, as we did with your mum. Speed with AML is of the essence; we need to stop it in its tracks if we're to have any hope of achieving remission.

We didn't achieve remission with the first cycle which was hugely disappointing. We quickly started a second cycle of chemotherapy, but sadly, that too has proved ineffective. Sally's leukaemia is resisting everything we throw at it and I'm afraid we have run out of options.'

Dr Clarke had told us nothing we didn't already know. He was going to tell us more whether he liked it or not.

'Um,' I cleared my throat. 'Hi, with all due respect we already know all of that. We're confused as to why there aren't any more drugs to try. We were initially told, and I quote "if we don't get it the first time we'll just keep trying until we do." We were told to expect up to six cycles. Mum has only had two.'

My heart was racing. I could feel the adrenaline pumping round my body. Dr Clarke reached up to scratch his head and then folded his arms across his protruding stomach.

'Yes, well, that *is* true in some cases. But we have to achieve remission or at least a partial remission with the first treatment cycle in order to continue with further cycles.'

'But that doesn't tie in with what we were told when my mum was first admitted.' My face was burning up. Dr Clarke winced.

'I'm very sorry if that wasn't properly explained to you.'

Laura looked puzzled.

'But you *did* administer another cycle.'

'Yes,' Dr Clarke stroked his speckled beard. 'We did. We were able to get hold of a drug that isn't used in standard treatment for AML, so we persisted. Unfortunately, this drug, like the first cycle of drugs, has failed to do any damage. Administering another cycle would, in our view, be futile.'

'But you don't know that,' Ray challenged, 'not for sure.'

Dr Clarke rocked back on his heels.

'No,' he admitted, 'not for sure, but we're fairly certain. Sally has had the strongest drugs available and due to her previous chemotherapy treatment for breast cancer it would be unwise to administer any more. There is a very real danger that her body wouldn't be able to withstand it.'

I glanced at Mum who hadn't said a word, and back at the consultant, 'But surely that's my mum's decision?'

'Ultimately, yes, but we wouldn't advise it.'

Silence.

'So,' Laura settled back into her chair and crossed her legs. 'Essentially, what you're saying is: Mum's cancer is untouchable and therefore untreatable.'

I closed my eyes and squeezed Mum's hand. Say no, say no.

Dr Clarke bowed his head slightly. 'Essentially, yes.'

Shit. I looked at Mum. She hadn't moved; her expression unaltered. What was she thinking? How was she feeling?

'And without treatment?'

Laura's voice broke before she could finish. Oh god, don't answer, don't answer. I locked eyes with Ray steeling myself for Dr Clarke's response.

'Without treatment,' he began 'it is, I'm very sorry to say, just a matter of time.'

I couldn't breathe. Bile leapt up into my throat. Ray shot up like a rocket, her hand clamped over her mouth, and ran out of the room. Mum's eyes misted over but she said nothing. Dr Clarke suddenly seemed very keen to leave.

'I can fetch a nurse if you'd like?'

Laura shook her head.

'No, no thank you.'

Dr Clarke nodded, walked out of the room and then quickly reappeared. 'Dr Humphreys will be around later if you have any further questions ...'

Laura and I just stared at him. I hated him. I barely knew him, but I hated him. Who the hell was he to tell us that Mum was a lost cause? That she couldn't withstand any more chemo? He didn't know her. He didn't know what she was capable of.

'So that's that then.'

Mum's voice was barely audible. She reached over to her bedside table, pulled a tissue from a box, lifted up her glasses and gently dabbed her eyes before rolling her head back onto her pillow.

'I always knew the third one would get me.'

CHAPTER 4

DECLARATIONS

Ray re-emerged a few minutes later all pink and blotchy and resumed her position at the other side of Mum's bed.

'Sorry,' she whispered.

Mum's face crumpled in pain. It was the first display of unguarded distress she'd shown, and my heart ripped at the sight of it.

'What for?' She asked, taking Ray's hands, and squeezing them. Ray lowered her head in shame.

'For crying,' she sniffed, 'and for leaving you.'

Mum shook her head.

'Oh darling, don't be silly.'

Tears spilled from Mum's eyes. And that was it. I gave in, completely and utterly.

'Mum, you can't die!' I heard myself shriek. 'You can't leave us!'

Fear whirled around inside of me as the unimaginable horror of what we'd been told finally took hold. Where was I? What was happening? I couldn't make any sense of it. The room shrunk. I couldn't feel my hands. My heart and head were racing.

'You can't die! You can't!'

I was wailing now and rocking in my chair. The outbursts just kept on coming.

'How am I supposed to carry on without you? How will I know what to do if you're not here?! You can't just simply cease to be!'

Mum's voice was clear as crystal.

'You'll find a way Kate-kins, you'll know what to do …'

How did she do it?! How and why was *she* comforting *me*?! It was *me* who should be comforting *her*! I slumped over onto the bed and sobbed for what seemed like days.

An elderly woman peered over the top of her square rimmed glasses and squinted hard at the cardboard juice carton she'd just been handed by her daughter.

'Apple?'

The daughter didn't respond.

'I don't like apple,' the older woman remarked. 'Didn't they have orange?'

Her daughter ignored her and instead set about cutting up her mother's anaemic-looking sausages.

'How can they not have orange?'

Silence.

'Are you *sure* they only had apple?' The mother persisted. 'I don't like apple.'

Her daughter sat back in her chair and looked out of the canteen window.

'They must have orange. Why don't you – '

'No Mum,' she barked. 'They don't have orange. If they did, I would have got it for you. They didn't, so I got you apple.'

The mother put down the unwanted carton.

'Okay dear, no need to shout.'

The daughter closed her eyes for a second before returning her gaze to the car park view from the window.

I had no idea who they were, but I hated them, both. I hated the older woman because she was old, and I hated her daughter because she was older than me and still had her mum. Neither of them knew what it was like to be without each other, to live in a world where the other didn't exist. Neither of them knew how lucky they were. My mum would never get old and at just thirty-one I would be without her, for the rest of my life.

'Have either of you got a paracetamol?' I asked my sisters.

My head was pounding. Ray continued to stare at the barely touched plate of soggy chips in front of her. Laura dived into her handbag and took out two capsules.

'Here you go.'

I swallowed them and quickly washed them down.

'Thanks.'

Laura picked up a chip, inspected it and bit the top off.

'You know,' she began, 'I think these chips, crap as they are, are the only edible option on the menu.'

I nodded.

'I've spent a fortune on them. And the muffins.' I took another swig of my water. 'I really should bring in my own food – it'd be a damn sight cheaper.'

I stole a glance at Ray. She looked awful. Laura didn't look much better. I dreaded to think how bad I must have looked. Picking up a knife, I peeked at my reflection. It wasn't pretty. I quickly put the knife back down.

Laura, Ray and I had been sat in the hospital canteen for about half an hour. We weren't hungry but Mum had insisted we get some food. So here we were, hunched around a little table. We were exhausted and, unusually for us, at a loss for words. The entire morning had been and gone, we'd sobbed, attempted and failed to soothe each other and sobbed some more.

'I need the loo,' Ray pushed back her chair, got up and walked towards the far end of the canteen. I watched her until she disappeared through the door. Poor little thing. Along with her bladder, which filled up faster than a Formula One car completing a lap at a Grand Prix, Ray's stomach was her Achilles heel; it's where she carried her stress. She'd been back and forth to the toilet all morning.

Laura had finished her chips and was sitting up with a purposeful expression on her face.

'We should probably call Dad.'

I wasn't so sure.

'She says she doesn't want to see him.'

'I know,' Laura replied, 'but he has to know what's going on.'

I started picking at the torn little bit of skin by my thumb.

'I suppose so. Do you want me to do it?' I said.

'You feel up to it?'

'Not really,' I admitted.

Laura shivered and started buttoning up her cardigan.

'I'll do it then,' she said. 'I've been keeping him informed up until now. I'll call him just before I leave.' She looked at her watch, 'Which should really be about now.'

Gathering up her things, she slung her bag over her shoulder and stood up to leave. I gave her a quick hug. 'I'm gonna stop in on Mum, then be on my way. Say bye to Ray for me.'

'Will do,' I replied.

She pulled me in for another hug.

'Call you later.'

I nodded and she was gone.

Mum and Dad's relationship was complicated, and, as a result, we all felt very protective towards her. The last thing any of us wanted was Dad upsetting her, especially now. They'd not spoken in months. Dad had pissed us all off over Christmas when he'd unexpectedly 'dumped' Mum the day after Boxing Day. They'd been getting on well before that and none of us had suspected a thing. Dad had decided that a life with Mum was no longer what he wanted. He'd experienced a world without her. In the year a half that they'd been apart he'd dated numerous women and had got serious with one of them, but after Mum had recovered from her double mastectomy last Spring, and had been given the all-clear, she'd seen Dad quite a bit and it looked like they were getting back together. Mum regularly stayed over at his flat and was even talking about moving back for good.

The fallout from the bombshell dumping was horrendous.

Mum was devastated and returned to Devon. I'd barely spoken to Dad since, not because I favoured my mum over my dad, but because I was angry with him. He just didn't seem to care about anything other than himself; he'd become a kind of 'sex symbol' amongst the fifty-something divorcees who danced their blues away at the weeknight swing and jive classes he'd long attended. He wasn't around when my sisters and I nursed and supported Mum through breast cancer and he very seldom checked in with any of us to see how *we* were doing. He knew Mum was sick and asked how she was, but that was about the extent of it. Mum made it clear she didn't want Dad around, which admittedly, made it hard for him to show his support, but we, his children, could have done with some.

I had it out with him in the February of last year following Mum's final chemo. I wrote him a letter and then met up with him to discuss it. He seemed truly dumbfounded and apologised. He checked in a lot more after that and he and Mum started talking again. So, with Mum's health and relationship with Dad back on track, we all relaxed a bit, believing the dark days to be behind us, but oh, how wrong we were. Three months after the dumping, Mum started complaining of headaches and a lack of energy. I wasn't overly worried; she'd been through a hell of a lot; it made sense to me that she'd be a bit run down, so I told her not to panic and to make an appointment with her GP. She did and two days later she and I were back at the hospital she'd been successfully treated at for breast cancer, awaiting the arrival of a Haematology consultant. Mum had Acute Myeloid Leukaemia and had been admitted within hours of the diagnosis. We were told it was 'imminently treatable' and that we had 'every reason to be optimistic.'

'Where's Laura?'

Ray's voice made me jump.

'She had to go,' I replied. 'Said to say bye and that she'd call us later.'

Ray sat down and started twisting a lock of her hair.

'We should get back to Mum.'

'Deffo,' I agreed. 'I'm going to call my boss first though, explain everything and let her know that I need some time off.'

Ray nodded.

'I should do that too.'

We had no idea what the next few days or weeks would entail, but if the doctors were right and Mum didn't have long, *I* was going nowhere. I worked for the cancer charity, Macmillan, so I was confident my boss and I would be able to come to some sort of agreement. I took a job there in the January of last year following Mum's breast cancer diagnosis, just a few months after I'd quit my job as a journalist at a local BBC radio station. Mum said she knew she had cancer the minute I'd resigned, believing that the universe was freeing me up to care for her. I had no idea she was sick when I made the decision to leave my job, so, although I was far from convinced, I could see where she was coming from.

Ray and I got up, tucked our chairs under the table and filed our dirty food trays in a stack of empty slots by the canteen kitchen. We took the stairs together, neither saying a word. At the entrance to Mum's ward, I paused by some communal seating. I removed my mobile from my pocket, looked up my work number and hoped for some love and understanding.

The afternoon was slow and painful. We talked about this and that but mostly we just sat in disbelieving silence, taking it in turn to weep or wail. The cancer had won. There was nothing we could do. At one point I drifted off and awoke to the soothing touch of Mum's hand lovingly stroking the top of my head. I stayed completely still and closed my eyes willing the moment to last forever. In the evening Ray and I were shown the family room. Grateful, we accepted and retreated to the room at about 10 pm. It was a sad, cold, uninviting little room. Paint was peeling from faded, yellow walls and the curtains were thin and uneven. In the corner, behind a make-do door, was a shabby looking toilet and wash basin. It was a room for the needy and the desperate. No joy or hope would be found and shared here. I brushed my teeth and attempted sleep. It didn't come. The night was long and restless; thoughts of what would no longer be, upset and tormented me. I gave up trying at daybreak, instead, fixing my gaze at the cracked and soiled ceiling above.

At about 7.30 I got up and walked into the washroom. I caught a glimpse of my reflection in the mirror above the sink and froze in shock. The face staring back at me was unrecognisable. Did it really belong to me? I never could pull off the 'just got out of bed' look. I needed work. But this was different; I looked deranged. My eyes were bloodshot, puffy and piggy small and my skin was sallow and blotchy. I couldn't really do much about my eyes, but I could certainly improve the unruly mop of matted hair sticking out from my head. I ran my fingers through it, smoothing out all the knots, and held the messy bundle I'd created with my left hand while removing a thin, black hair band from my right wrist with my teeth. I then wound the band securely around the lump I'd created. Satisfied, I splashed my face with cold water, located my make-up bag and applied moisturiser and foundation, generously. I took a step back and squinted at my reflection. There was no hiding it, I looked bad, really bad. But it was nothing compared to the wreck inside. Ray was suddenly standing beside me. She leaned over the sink for a closer inspection and grimaced.

'Yuck.'

Yeah right. It was true she looked far from great, but Ray's worst had nothing on your average person's best; she was neat and pretty, end of.

'You've nothing on me, baby sis,' I challenged her. 'I look like I've just been dug up! Do you think they'll let me back on the ward? I wouldn't want to make life even more unpleasant for the patients.'

Ray let out a giggle and then immediately stopped. I knew what she was thinking. We weren't supposed to giggle. We had nothing to giggle about. Tears pricked the back of my eyes. Ray wrapped her arms around me and squeezed hard. Neither of us wanted to let go. We clung to each other in that pokey little washroom for what seemed like hours. Would we get through this? Would we ever again laugh like we used to? We finished getting ready and made our way slowly and apprehensively back to Mum's bedside.

CHAPTER 5

HOPE

Ray and I sat and stared at the coal burner in front of us, dumbfounded. Why couldn't we get the damn thing to stay alight? Mum never had a problem with it; she revelled in the sodding thing. Ray puffed out her cheeks.

'What now?'

I threw my hands up in the air, defeated.

'Beats me.'

'We've done everything we're supposed to,' Ray reasoned. 'Why isn't it working?'

I had no answer. We'd cleared out the grate at the bottom, loaded it up with fresh coal, firelighters and kindling wood; poked and prodded at the coal to encourage it to take, but all to no avail. Sparks came and went, like shooting stars, and we'd been forced to start over, again and again. It was 11 pm – we'd been at it for over an hour. We had little choice – the coal burner heated the house. If we couldn't get it to work, we'd freeze. I kicked the glass door with my foot, 'bloody thing.'

This wretched coal burner, along with the wood burner in the lounge, were a continual source of irritation. They were like toddlers – difficult and demanding. I'd lost many, many hours tending to their every whim. 'Put another log on Kate-kins', 'Give it a good poke Kate-kins', it just went on and on; I was up and down from Mum's dog-scratched leather couch like a bloody yo-yo. I'd tut and curse, but Mum would just laugh and insist they were worth it. I was yet to be convinced.

'Maybe Phil can help us get it working in the morning?' Ray said and took a sip of her tea. 'We can ask him to take a look at it when he pops in to feed the dogs. Not that he needs to do that now.'

Phil, was Mum's neighbour. He lived opposite and kept an eye on the dogs, letting them out and feeding them, whenever Mum was away. He'd been a lifesaver these past few months. He said it was nothing; he was retired and spent most of his time pottering in his garden and ferrying his disabled wife to and from hospital appointments.

'Let's keep it from Mum though,' I said. 'It'll worry her, and we don't need to trouble her with it.'

Ray nodded and rubbed her eyes. It'd been a long day. We'd sat at Mum's bedside, dipped in and out of stilted conversation and waited for time to pass. I'd been granted thirty days compassionate leave from work, as had Ray. We had no idea what was going to happen, but we'd be living and breathing it all together.

Time to turn in. I got up from the padded, wooden chair I'd been sat on and patted my bum in a bid to revive it. It was well and truly numb. 'God,' I sighed. 'I'd kill for a shower.' I closed my eyes and imagined it; a shower was completely out of the question. Not only did we have no hot water, Mum didn't own one. She had a flimsy, rubber, makeshift shower-head attachment thing that screwed loosely and limply onto the bath taps. You had to sit in the bath and hose yourself down with it like it was 1952. I'd rather stink than experience it. And washing your hair took forever. The water flow was little more than a lifeless trickle and the temperature was decidedly temperamental. I often opted for what Mum called a 'whore's wash' (a quick wash of the essentials in a shallow bath). Satisfying? No. Hygienic? Ish. Hassle free? Abso-bloody-lutely! Mum was planning to install a shower in the little room by the kitchen downstairs; a project that, like so many, would now cease to be. To be honest, the whole house needed a major facelift. Structurally it was okay, but the inside? Sad and tired. Mum believed it had a lot of potential and had made a solid start on some basic interior renovation, livening up the hallway with bright yellow paint. The cottage windows were small and let in little light and the new sunny walls made a big difference. She was about to get going on the lounge when the hospital called with her blood results. Perhaps we could do a bit of work while we were here?

Darcy stalked into the kitchen, sniffing the air. It was the first time I'd seen her. She stopped in front of me and lifted her eyes to meet mine.

'Why hello your highness, to what do I owe this pleasure?'

Ray snickered.

'Probably hungry.'

I patted the top of Darcy's nose.

'Hungry?'

Darcy just continued to eyeball me.

'Get her a treat from the cupboard,' Ray suggested. 'I'll fill up her water bowl.'

I opened the cupboard and found a bag of half-eaten chews. I shook the bag in front of her 'Want one?' There was a scuffle and a bang, and less than a second later Wilf was standing in front of me drooling and wagging his tail.

I laughed, 'you don't miss a trick do you Wilf?'

He jabbed me in the thigh with his dewy nose. 'Alright, alright!' I took out a chew and waved it in front of him leading his eyes from side to side. Wilf started making a frantic, whining nose.

'Don't be mean,' Ray said with a smile. 'Just give it to him.'

'That'd be too easy,' I replied. 'He doesn't do any tricks, useless mutt, so he can wait a bit longer, suffer along with the rest of us.'

Ray was properly laughing now. Darcy, as usual, did nothing. I wasn't even sure she wanted a chew. 'Has she *got* a brain?' I teased. Ray bent down and hugged her.

'They both have tiny heads,' she replied, defensive on their behalf, 'so there's not much room.'

It was my turn to laugh. Wilf's eyes darted from me to the chew and back again. The desperation was comical. I shook my head and dropped the chew on the floor. Wilf, in rocket speed, swooped down and chomped at it. I did the same in front of Darcy. She slowly lowered her head and cautiously inspected it like she was assessing an undetonated bomb.

I rolled my eyes, 'Oh for God's sake dog, it's not going to

kill you. Eat it!' Ray, giggling, picked it up and put the chew to Darcy's mouth, encouraging her to try it.

'Come on Darcy,' she cooed. 'Eat it.'

Eventually Darcy took the chew and trotted back to wherever she'd come from. 'You're welcome!' I shouted after her. 'No, no really, it was no trouble at all.' And then in a more hushed tone 'ungrateful wretch.'

'Ah, Gus-Gus,' Ray leant over and kissed my cheek, 'you do make me laugh.'

I awoke to the sound of voices. I propped myself up on to my elbows and frantically scanned the room. The voices were male and merry. I reached for my mobile. It was a little after three in the morning. Muffled laughter. I ducked down under my duvet. It was highly unusual to hear anything here at night. The road was home to just a few and they certainly weren't the type of people to be walking around and laughing in the middle of the night. I shivered. My eyes were quickly adjusting to the light. I should check, look out the window and see what is going on. I looked over at Ray, she is sound asleep. Damn it. More voices. My heart started pounding hard. I licked my lips. I hated the dark, or rather what I imagined *lurked* in the dark. As a teenager, I dreaded the walk home from my Saturday job at Clarks shoe shop, utterly convinced that I would end my days in a layby or dumpster after being dragged off the street by some lowlife nutter. Thankfully, I was a little braver these days and no longer allowed my imagination to get the better of me. That said, there were occasions when I faltered, and as my heart rate quickened it was becoming apparent that tonight I could very well succumb.

'Ray?' I whispered, hoping she'd wake and deal with it.

I tried again 'Ray?' Nothing.

Perhaps I hadn't heard anything? The dogs weren't barking, not that I could rely on that. Wilf and Darcy didn't really bark, preferring to whine, and offered about as much protection as a chocolate fire guard. Laughter. Shit! I took a deep breath, flung off the duvet and swung my legs out and over the edge of the bed. I slowly raised myself up and tiptoed towards the window. I didn't want to look. I closed my eyes willing myself to slide back the curtain.

'Gus?'

Holy shit! I jumped back a foot. Ray was sitting up in bed and staring straight at me.

'Jesus, Ray,' I hissed. 'You scared the bloody life out of me!'

I pressed the palm of my hand on my chest to calm my nerves.

'Sorry,' Ray whispered, 'but what are you doing?'

What was I doing? Good question. Ray was awake. I felt a little less panicked. 'I heard voices and was checking it out.'

'Voices?' Ray repeated. I nodded and pointed to the window. 'Right outside.'

I raised my hand to the curtain and slowly pulled it to one side. I pushed my head through the gap and looked up and down the road. There was no one there.

'Well?'

I wrinkled up my face in confusion and looked again, first left then right. Strange. How could no one be there? I heard voices, lots of them, several times. I closed the curtain, straightened up and got back into bed. 'I must have imagined it.'

'Or,' Ray replied, 'whoever it was has walked on further up the road and out of sight …'

Hmmm, I didn't like that idea.

'Maybe.' I pulled the duvet up towards my chin. Ray did the same.

'It's sooooo cold,' she said through chattering teeth. 'I've got on two pairs of socks, a T-shirt and two jumpers and I'm *still* cold. I hope we can get the boiler working tomorrow.'

I hoped so too. I also hoped I'd fall quickly back to sleep. No such luck.

'Gus?' There was panic in Ray's voice. 'Did you hear that?'

'Hear what?' I replied, fearful of the answer. There was a slight pause.

'Sounded like a horse and cart.'

'What?!'

'A horse and cart …'

We were going mad. No doubt about it. It was the only possible explanation. I smiled. This realisation instantly calmed me.

'Gus?'

'Yes?'

'I'm scared.'

I reached for Ray's hand and squeezed it. 'Put it out of your head, Ray. This house, like everything else at the moment, is just a little fucked up.'

'So,' Ray began, 'I've heard back from that AML specialist I contacted in London yesterday and he reckons Mum's case is far from over. He says if she feels strong enough the doctors should administer an alternative drug combination – even if the drugs they have left aren't, as the docs say here, 'the big guns.' He says we all respond differently to different drugs and if Mum was *his* patient, he'd try something else.'

I wanted to jump up and punch the air like a guitar God. This was *exactly* what we'd been waiting for! This man wasn't just anybody, he was an AML expert, not a haematologist, an AML expert. A man who specialised in the disease, who dealt with it day in, day out and therefore, in my mind, carried a helluva lot more clout than the current crop of dismissive general 'blood' consultants in charge of Mum's treatment. This man was superior; his opinion outranked them all. I felt a little giddy.

'And that's not all!' Ray rushed on. 'He thinks Mum's AML should have been treated as a secondary cancer from the onset. He is in little doubt that Mum developed the disease from the chemo treatment she was given for breast cancer, cos of the speed in which she contracted it. Apparently, he sees the connection quite often and this offers a plausible explanation as to why she responded so badly to the first cycle.'

Ray looked up at me from the piece of paper she was holding all wide eyed and hopeful. I swallowed hard and stared back at her, disbelieving. Mum's brow furrowed.

'They've been pumping me full of the drug that actually *gave* me the disease?'

We exchanged puzzled expressions and took a moment to digest this startling possibility. Is this really what might have happened? If so, no wonder she'd responded so poorly! Mum's first cycle was a disaster. Lesions broke out all over her face and she suffered a full-on fever, it was as if the drugs were making everything worse. I felt flushed with adrenaline. It had all become clear: the drugs they gave Mum in the first cycle didn't work cos they were the same drugs that gave her AML in the first place.

'Exactly!' I exclaimed. 'They fought fire with fire and made the whole thing worse!' I leapt from my seat and quickly sat back down again. I wasn't quite sure what to do with myself. Ray was grinning like a Cheshire cat, eyes sparkling with excitement.

'Oh my God!'

'I know!' I squealed, leaning over, and rubbing Mum's arm with my other hand. Mum was staring straight ahead, eyes moist and vacant. I willed her to respond and after a couple of minutes, she did.

'So,' she began, eyes still fixed straight ahead 'I can have more treatment.'

It was a statement rather than a question, but Ray and I nodded back eagerly in response. The tide had turned. 'The doctors here might not go for it,' I warned 'but we can try and convince them.' I pointed at Ray's piece of paper 'more treatment's recommended *and* according to this AML expert in treating your cancer as a primary they've quite possibly, and more than majorly, fucked up.' I cupped Mum's hand, lifted it and kissed it. 'The power's with *us*.' I felt ten feet tall. This battle was ours for the taking. We were sitting at a major crossroad; the fight far from over. I grabbed Ray's hand and raised it up towards the ceiling in an act of determined and triumphant solidarity. Tears were streaming down her cheeks. I closed my eyes. Hope had returned.

The consultants were divided. We'd presented our desire to push on with more treatment to Dr Langham – a dumpy, kindly looking middle-aged man with a full head of grey and black speckled hair – the following morning. He promised to discuss Mum's case with the five other consultants at their weekly round-up meeting later that very afternoon. It was 5 pm and three out of the six were now crowded into Mum's room debating it.

'I'm mostly concerned,' said the only female consultant, 'that Sally's liver won't be able to withstand it.'

'This is a very valid concern,' agreed Dr Humphreys. 'However, if Sally says she's up for more treatment, then ultimately, it's her call.'

'I disagree,' came the female doctor's reply. 'Sally has already had two rounds of chemo and I'd be unhappy administering any more. She's barely recovered from the last round.'

An alarmingly tall man with sparse, wispy hair, stepped forward. His name, I later found out, was Dr Williams.

'Dr Clarke and I, whom, I'm sorry, but couldn't be with us this evening, are of the shared mind that more treatment is certainly doable. There is a chance that Sally's AML *is* a secondary cancer and not a primary cancer as we first thought, and therefore we may, and I stress *may* have more luck tackling it with a different cocktail of drugs, but there's no way of knowing.'

Dr Williams gripped onto the rail at the end of Mum's bed with both hands. 'And Dr Turner is right to be concerned about administering more chemo – the body can only withstand so much, and you've already had more than most. The worst-case scenario is that another cycle would seriously compromise the quality of life that you have left – '

'But,' Ray interjected, 'the *best* case scenario is that another cycle could wipe out the cancer for good and give my mum her life back.'

I wanted to hug her. For the last half an hour we'd been bombarded with medical jargon and a 'glass half empty' attitude. We knew more chemo was a risk, but as Ray had so brilliantly and simply put it, it was, without doubt, a risk worth taking.

All three consultants seemed stumped. Dr Williams was now standing up straight, the top of his head just millimetres from the ceiling, and was rubbing his chin in contemplation. The woman, Dr Turner, was biting the tip of a biro and Dr Humphreys was leaning, arms crossed against the wall. Had we convinced them? Laura was listening to the discussion via my mobile phone. I'd filled her in earlier and she wanted to be a part of it. She asked to be put on speakerphone.

'So,' she began, 'it sounds as though the only concern you *really* have is my mum's ability to withstand more chemo. Correct? And if she says she's willing to take the risk, decision made.'

We stared at Dr Williams, eagerly awaiting his response. He took a big breath before he spoke.

'Well, yes, in a way, but there is our duty of care to consider and the cost of the drugs,' a slight pause. 'Your mum is not the only patient at the hospital.'

His words were like a slap in the face.

'We lobbied the PCT hard for the specialist drug used in Sally's second cycle,' he continued, 'there's no guarantee they'd support another round *especially* as the first two cycles failed.'

'Convince them!?' Laura barked through the telephone.

Dr Williams let out a nervous laugh. It was my turn.

'Dr Williams, please, we have to try. The first cycle doesn't really count. There's a chance she *could* still beat this. Don't give up on her, please.'

The consultants exchanged glances.

'Dr Williams,' we turned to face Mum, who up until now had barely said a word, 'I can handle it.'

Ray and I smiled with pride. Mum could do this, she knew it, we knew it and we'd be right here with her, every step of the way. A small, affectionate smile tugged at the corners of Dr Williams' mouth.

'You're a determined bunch, aren't you?'

Ray and I beamed at him. We'd won. Dr Williams held up both hands in mock surrender.

'Okay, okay, we'll see what we can do, but no promises.' We nodded, expressed our thanks, and watched them all leave. My body slumped with relief.

'Girls,' Mum was sitting up and looking at us with a steely intent, 'Call your father,' she instructed. 'I want to see him.'

CHAPTER 6

DAD

I was squatting next to my car in the hospital car park, staring at my mobile, Mum's words echoing in my ears. 'I need him girls, I need you all. Call him.'

I ran a hand through my hair and looked up at the blue, cloudless sky. I hadn't spoken to Dad in such a long time. I was just so angry with him. I couldn't face it. But Mum needed him. She didn't elaborate, just asked me to call him and get him here. It was a complete U-turn. Up until now she'd point blank refused to see him. She was vulnerable, her health critical. I feared Dad's arrival would upset the status quo and distress her, but it was her wish, and I wasn't about to argue with her. I just had to pluck up the courage and call. I took a couple of deep breaths. It really shouldn't be this hard, he is my dad, for goodness' sake! I shook my head, stood up with a confidence I didn't possess and located his number in my address book. I hovered over the dial key for a couple of seconds to gather my thoughts. Keep it short and to the point. Dad answered straight away.

'Kate?'

He sounded a little anxious.

'Hi Dad,' my palms were sweaty. 'How are you?'

'Okay,' he replied, 'but more importantly, how are you?'

Well, that was unexpected.

'Um,' I wasn't sure how best to answer. 'Not bad,' I paused, 'considering.'

'What's happening?'

Dad's voice was full of a concerned urgency, and it threw me.

'I,' Fuck, this was hard. 'Um,' I was faltering.

'Kate?'

I closed my eyes, willing myself on.

'Mum,' I began. 'She wants to see you.'

Silence, then finally.

'Good, good,' his voice cracked. 'When?'

'Right away.' I felt for the safety of my car behind me. 'She says she needs you.'

It had suddenly got very noisy.

'Just a second Kate. Good afternoon, madam, how can I help?'

The woman was looking for a frame for her photo. 'No problem,' I heard Dad reply. 'They're just over there in the corner. What size?'

I couldn't hear the woman's response cos Dad started shouting, 'Steve, Steve, can you assist this lady, please? Sorry, madam, I've got to continue with this phone call.'

This is how calls with Dad at work always went. He'd suddenly break away from conversation to assist a customer. It was a little annoying, but I understood. It was the same when talking to Laura at home. No call was complete without some sort of interruption from one of her kids, unless the call took place in the evening, when the boys were in bed.

'Sorry about that, Kate. I'm in the studio now, so I'm all yours.'

'That's okay,' I replied. 'So, how soon can you get here?'

I could hear him flicking through his diary.

'I've got a meeting this evening, so I can leave at dawn, get to you mid-morning. Is that okay?'

I was a bit disappointed. Why couldn't he cancel the meeting and drive down now?

'Yeah,' I lied.

'Is she okay?' Dad pressed. 'I'm desperate to see her. I've been going out my mind since Laura told me they'd stopped treatment. I'm so relieved she wants to see me.'

My throat tightened, but I was determined to remain firm and unrattled.

'You can't upset her,' I warned. 'You have to forget about everything's that's happened. I think she believes you can help her, so that's what you have to do.'

'I have no intention of upsetting her. Why would I?'

I could feel a knot forming in the pit of my stomach.

'I'm not saying you will. She's scared, Dad, she's vulnerable. It's a delicate situation and you haven't seen each other or spoken to each other for months.'

'Kate, trust me, I just want to see her, sit with her and hold her hand.' Dad let out a sad sigh before continuing, 'Your mother and I go back a long way.'

I felt a bit silly. I wanted the call to end.

'We'll see you tomorrow then,' I replied matter-of-factly. 'Call me when you're near and I'll let you know where we are. Parking's a bit of a pain, but you'll find a space eventually.'

'Righto,' Dad was smiling; I could hear it. 'Looking forward to it.'

I wasn't sure if I was.

'Yep,' I managed, in a clipped, uncertain tone. 'See you soon.'

I flipped shut my mobile and slumped against my car, sliding slowly and deliberately all the way down to the ground. The call, thank goodness, had been a success. I tipped my head up to the sky and took a couple of minutes to enjoy the glorious heat from the sun. It felt good. It felt healing. I stayed a few minutes longer and smiled to myself. Perhaps everything was going to be okay after all ...

Mum looked beautiful. How on earth was this possible? She was terminally ill. For the last hour we'd been dolling her up, ready for Dad's arrival. She said she didn't want Dad to see her 'all ill looking', and she certainly didn't want him to see her without hair. I was so used to her bald little head I'd almost forgotten what she looked like *with* hair. I almost preferred it. Mum had visibly relaxed the minute I told her Dad was coming, so much so that for the first time since we'd arrived back in Devon, we watched a film, some crappy sentimental claptrap about a high-powered-businesswoman jacking in her job to renovate a run-down villa in Italy. This morning though, Mum was a little more tense. She fretted over her outfit. 'The brown cardigan or the green?' and took her time applying mascara and blue kohl to the rims of her eyes. I'd wrapped a green scarf around her head and plaited it to one side fastening it in place with two gold star-shaped clips that I had found in a basket on her dresser at home. It was all quite sweet; like a teenager getting ready for a first date. But to be honest, I wasn't really sure *what* to make of it. Their relationship had stopped making sense to me a while ago, but it was clear from Mum's fussing that she still cared what Dad thought of her and especially what he thought of her appearance. Mum was a glamour puss. She took care of herself and although Dad complained heavily over her spending, he loved that she always made an effort and impressed. Mum often said he enjoyed her good looks a bit too much. He didn't see past her big, beautiful eyes; couldn't see and didn't know the person behind them. His inability to 'delve a little deeper' was, as far as I could see, the overriding cause of Mum's frustration with him. He didn't understand her, she'd lament over and over. He didn't truly get what made her tick. My sisters and I had heard it all countless times. Yet, here she was, all a tizz, applying rusty red lippy and geeing herself up for her meeting with Dad.

'I don't think I want your dad to come to the ward.'

Mum's eyes were flicking about nervously.

'Okay,' I said. 'But I'm not sure we really have a choice.'

Mum's eyes rested on a wheelchair outside her room and pointed towards it.

'We could go outside,' she suggested. 'It'd be nice to feel a bit of sun.'

Her eyes locked onto mine awaiting a response.

'We could,' I replied, cautiously. 'But you're not supposed to go in the sun, remember? Your skin's too sensitive after all the chemo.'

Mum had clearly already thought about this.

'I'll be wearing a cardy and my head will be covered.'

I looked over at Ray who was swirling a tea bag around in a paper cup.

'Sounds like a good idea to me,' she said. Ray put down her cup and stood up. 'I'll ask the nurse and check it's okay.'

Mum beamed like a little girl who had masterfully outfoxed her parents.

'I think you should wear the brown cardy,' I suggested. 'But do it up, it's quite breezy out.'

I reached over and helped her put it on, our roles one hundred per cent reversed.

'You okay?' I asked, tilting my head in concern.

Mum pulled a face as if to say, 'not sure, but we'll soon find out.'

My phone beeped. It was Dad. He was here. Ray came bouncing back into the room, accompanied by a young, smiley male nurse with a barely there goatee.

'We can go outside – '

'As long as it's not for too long,' the nurse interjected. 'We don't want you tiring yourself out.'

I stood up and offered him my hand. I hadn't seen him before. 'Hi,' I said, sweetly.

He reached out and shook it, 'Hi,' he said, brightly, 'name's Steve.'

Mum smiled up at him.

'Hi!'

'Ah,' replied Steve, 'you must be Sally, I've heard lots about you.' He looked over at me and winked. Mum blushed.

'Really?'

'Oh yeah,' Steve continued. 'You and your gorgeous, giggly girls are the talk of the ward.'

Mum cocked her head to one side and narrowed her eyes. Steve chuckled and turned to retrieve the wheelchair in the hallway outside Mum's room. 'All good, mam, I assure you.' Steve locked the wheelchair in place with his foot and looked first at me and then Ray, 'Do either of you know how to work these things?'

I shook my head and wished I'd made more of an effort with my appearance.

'Nope,' said Ray.

'No worries,' Steve assured us. 'It's simple. Your mum's feet rest on these and if you want to park the wheelchair just flip the break, down here,' he said pointing to his foot which was resting on a lever.

I fiddled with my fringe and flashed him a big toothy smile, 'Cool.' He was the first good-looking male I'd seen in a while, and I couldn't help myself. Steve smiled back.

'Where are you gonna go?' Steve asked.

'Not sure,' I replied.

'The area by the duck pond is nice, towards the back of the hospital. There's quite a bit of shade there too.'

Wow. He was so lovely. This is how all hospital staff should be. His smiley disposition and helpful, casual approach made such a difference.

'Thank you,' I said sincerely.

'No probs,' Steve bowed his head at me. 'Ready Sally?'

Mum nodded eagerly and slowly stood up. Steve gave Mum his arm and lowered her into the chair.

'Okay?' He asked, squatting so he was face to face with her.

'Yep,' Mum replied. 'Thank you.'

Ray pushed her out of the room and hollered back at me.

'Better tell Dad where to meet us.'

Steve motioned for me to follow Ray.

'After you. Have fun.'

I smiled my sweetest smile.

'Will do.'

I decided not to text Dad right away; I wanted us to reach the duck pond first and get settled. There was a map of the hospital on the wall next to the elevator. I studied it and mentally walked through the route. A few minutes later we were outside and rolling Mum down a steep path towards the duck pond. Ray almost lost control of the wheelchair a few times on the way down, the sudden weight of it taking her by surprise, but thankfully, and much to our relief, she never let go completely. The wheelchair also had a wonky wheel making it impossible to steer, like a misbehaving shopping trolley. Ray rammed Mum into a wall at one point which had us all doubled over and chuckling. Once we were at the bottom of the path, we made a sharp left and the duck pond sprung into view. It was a large pond and was surrounded, as you'd expect, by tall trees and grassy banks. There was a bench on a little island in the centre. Perfect. I pointed at it.

'Shall we sit there? It's half in the sun and half in the shade,' I said.

Mum nodded and Ray steered her, without incident, towards it. While Ray helped Mum onto the bench, I removed my mobile from my back pocket and typed and sent a text to Dad confirming our location and arrival. I then positioned myself on Mum's right, boxing her in, protecting her. I stole a quick glance at Ray and started drumming the table. My stomach was alive with butterflies. Dad would be here any minute. I fixed my gaze at the top of the grassy bank and waited for him to emerge.

Dad walked swiftly into view lit from behind by the sun. He stopped, scanned the area, spotted me, smiled, and waved. He rolled up the sleeves of his yellow, V-neck, fitted jumper and strutted down the bank towards us. He looked strong and healthy. I stole a quick glance at Mum; the contrast was startling. His pace quickened as he approached the island, the smile on his face big and bright. If he was nervous, he wasn't letting it show. A shaft of sunlight had found a route through the trees behind us and was warming Mum's forearm. I gently nudged her elbow to the left of the beam, keeping her from harm.

'Wotcha, kiddo.'

Dad was standing directly in front of us, hands on his hips

and staring straight at Mum. She smiled weakly in return. Time to go.

I looked up at Dad. 'We'll leave you to it,' I said and squeezed Mum's shoulder as I got up to leave. 'We'll be right over there,' I told her. 'Where you can see us.'

Mum nodded and smiled. She suddenly looked so small and fragile. Dad had better behave.

'Make sure she isn't exposed to the sun,' I warned and made my way to the grassy bank opposite, Ray just a couple of feet behind.

We tried to distract ourselves by making daisy chains and silly shadows in the sun, but it was hard to resist peeking over and speculating. As soon as we'd gone Dad had quickly sat down next to Mum and pulled her into an embrace. Mum burrowed into him and wept, Dad gently stroking her and kissing the top of her head. They stayed like that, locked in each other's arms, for ages, Mum occasionally breaking away to look up at him and say something. I desperately wanted to know what. But it heartened me to see them together. It was so familiar. Mum looked safe and somewhat relieved. Dad pointed towards something, and she laughed, loud and hard. Ray and I grinned at each other. We hadn't heard her laugh like that in such a long time. I wasn't sure she ever would again. But Dad had found a way in. He'd succeeded where we had failed. I shivered. The warmth from the sun was fading, Mum would be cold.

'I think we need to get Mum back inside,' I said to Ray and waved over at them both.

They smiled and beckoned us over. I was right – Mum was covered in goose pimples. Ray resumed her position behind the wheelchair as Dad helped her climb into it. Dad took over the pushing at the bottom of the hill, rolling Mum up it with little effort. It was a considerate and controlling move and one that both surprised and delighted me. Ray and I held hands and skipped on ahead.

'Oh my god!' exclaimed Ray. 'It's amazing!'

It really was. While we'd been at the duck pond Steve the nurse had sketched a cartoon on the white board opposite Mum's bed. We knew Steve had done it because he'd signed it in the bottom right-hand corner. It was of a nurse holding up a giant syringe with the caption: 'Doris was pleased she'd found a way to sneak in that vodka.' Mum found it hilarious. We were all still laughing about it when Dr Williams shuffled into the room.

'Good to hear you all laughing,' he said, as he positioned himself at the foot of Mum's bed. Mum wiped a happy tear from her eye and pointed towards the sketch behind him.

'We'd nipped out for a bit of fresh air and came back to that.'

Dr Williams looked over his left shoulder, considered it and snickered.

'Very good.' He peered at the sketch a little longer. 'Steve, hmm, must be one of the nurses.'

'He is,' I gushed, 'and a very lovely nurse he is too.'

I sounded like some idiotic teenage girl with a crush, but

really, I was just keen to sell his virtues higher up the chain; get him some acknowledgement. Dr Williams nodded and turned back to face us resting his gaze suspiciously on Dad.

'I'm Tony,' said Dad, reaching out his hand. 'Sally's husband.'

Dr Williams shook his hand.

'Right,' he replied, sounding somewhat confused. I suppose it *was* a bit strange. There had been no mention of a husband up until now. Dr Williams probably assumed, if he assumed anything at all, that there wasn't one.

'Are you okay, Sally, for me to say what I need to in front of your husband?'

Mum, who was sitting up dutifully, nodded vehemently.

'Of course!'

Dr Williams held up a hand in defence.

'Just checking,' he said. 'We can never be too careful.'

I was a little taken aback. This was the most tact from a consultant I'd seen the whole time I'd been here.

'My fellow consultants and I put your case and request for more treatment before the PCT yesterday and the board came back to us this morning with a decision.'

We all held our breath.

'They've approved our request, and treatment,' Dr Williams smiled before continuing, 'will begin tomorrow.'

My hands flew up to my face, tears pooled in my eyes. We'd done it. Mum had another shot. I wanted to jump up, fling my arms around him and shower him with grateful kisses.

'We'll need to change your line first thing, but a nurse will talk you through this later.' Dr Williams paused. 'Happy?'

We all nodded.

'Good.' Dr Williams rubbed his hands together. 'I'll leave you to it then,' he said and sloped off out of the room. Ray was on her feet and clapping.

'Yay!'

Mum and Dad were gazing lovingly at each other like a couple of honeymooners, hands knitted tightly together. It suddenly struck me. Dad was Mum's protector, and this is what Mum had been missing. She had no parents. Her dad, who she'd adored, died from a heart attack when she just twenty-six years old, and her mum – a trusted and much-needed confidant – passed away six years ago, close to Mum's fiftieth. Mum had no one to turn to. Yes, she had us, and we were a big help and comfort, but we were her children, *she* looked after us. Mum needed more, she needed the love and support of someone she'd always known; someone who could wrap her up like a little girl and tell her everything was going to be okay. We couldn't do this, but Dad could.

They'd met when they were fourteen at an ice rink in Greater London. Mum was a skinny, big-eyed beauty and Dad fell for her instantly. He worked at the rink and impressed with a charm and confidence that belied his teenage years. Mum and Dad were inseparable. They married young and surged through life with passion and purpose, buying and selling several properties before purchasing their final home – a four-bed cottage in a small residential town in Surrey with an acre of land. As kids, we wanted for nothing. Dad made the money and Mum made the home. It was idyllic and drama free, up until we all left home, not that I or my sisters were ever fully aware of what was going on or how Mum was truly feeling; we were way too busy forging ahead with our own lives. It was my gran's death and the removal of a dodgy mole that seemed to kick it all off. Her drinking, which had never been heavy, dramatically increased, and grumbles about Dad – what he had or hadn't done – started to creep regularly into conversations. It became quite difficult to listen to – nothing I said ever seemed to be taken on board. It was all very needy. I wrongly convinced myself she was 'attention seeking' and after a while, instead of helping her work through it all I decided to put some distance between us. Something I've regretted and tried to make up for ever since. We still talked and had fun at family get-togethers, but phone calls were short and far less frequent. It wasn't that I didn't care; I just didn't think she truly wanted the help. Laura and Ray handled it all in their own way, but we all agreed it was exhausting, frustrating and ultimately, horribly upsetting. Watching them now, Dad gently caressing Mum's cheek, doting on her every word, it was clear love was still very much there. Theirs was a bond too strong to break; the power of it overwhelmed me – it was literally bringing her back to life.

'What are you smiling at?'

Mum asked, eyes twinkling. I wasn't aware that I *was* smiling.

'Me?' I shrugged my shoulders, 'nothing really, just happy.'

Mum beamed back at me.

'Me too.'

She then reached out and covered my hand with hers.

'Why don't you both go home, relax, eat a proper dinner. You've been at this hospital with me twenty-four seven for five days. Dad's here now, go back to the house, chill out in front of the fire.'

Ray scoffed and rolled her eyes. Mum looked at us both quizzically.

'The fire,' I began, 'is a big fat pain the butthole. We can get it going, but we can't get it to stay alight overnight.'

Mum's eyes widened in alarm.

'Why didn't you say?! You should have told me! Have you got enough kindling? Cleaned out the debris at the bottom of the grate?'

'Yes, yes,' I replied. 'A thousand times, but it just won't stay alight.'

'Phil got it working for us a couple of days ago,' Ray interjected, 'but when we start fiddling with it in the evening it goes out.'

Mum pursed her lips together, clearly annoyed. 'Sort it for them, love,' she said to Dad. 'Find out what's wrong with it.' Mum tutted and shook her head.

'You should have said something.'

Ray got up and arched her back, 'Oh Gus,' she said dreamily, rolling her neck from side to side. 'Just imagine, a proper dinner.'

'The food here that good, eh?' said Dad.

Ray looked at Dad and nodded sarcastically. 'Oh yeah, the best,' she teased. 'If you're lucky one or two chips may *actually* be cooked.'

'And for afters,' I added, 'there's always the queue-up-so-you-don't-miss-it restaurant staple – muffin in a bowl of thick, lumpy custard!' I licked my lips theatrically, 'It's to die for …'

'Mmmmm,' said Dad, rubbing his stomach, 'can't wait!'

Chuckling, I got up out of my chair and slung my handbag over my shoulder. I was already at the cottage, boots off, tucked up on the sofa. I bent over and gave Mum a kiss. 'If you're sure?'

Mum nodded furiously. 'Yes, yes, go – I insist.'

'Okay,' I replied and walked over to a pin board loosely attached to the wall opposite Mum's bed. Twenty pins had been arranged into the shape of a palm tree. I'm not sure who started it, but it had become customary to rearrange the pins into something new every time one of us left the room. I thought about it for a second or two and settled on creating a shooting star. Tomorrow was going to be a big day. I looked back at Mum as soon as I'd finished.

'Wish on it before you go to sleep,' I instructed, and with Ray in tow, happily headed for home.

CHAPTER 7

CYCLE THREE

'What?!' I screamed. 'No way! You can't have that! It's not even a word!'

Mum, Dad, Laura, Ray and I were huddled around Mum's bed playing Scrabble when Laura put down an 'x' followed by an 'i'.

'Yes, it is a word,' Laura insisted.

'Yeah?' I challenged, 'What does it mean?'

Laura sat back in her chair looking pleased with herself.

'It's a Chinese word,' she said, confidently. 'I'm not *entirely* sure of its meaning, but it *is* allowed.'

I narrowed my eyes at her.

'If it's not in the *English* dictionary, it's *not* allowed.'

Laura folded her arms.

'It's a classic Scrabble word, Mark and I use it all the time.'

'Mark,' I reminded her, 'is a renowned cheat!'

'True,' Laura agreed, eyes dancing with mischief. 'But I assure you in Scrabble Xi *is* a legitimate word.'

I wasn't convinced. And with nine points at stake, I wasn't prepared to give in without a fight. 'I say we vote on it. Ray?'

'Erm,' Ray pulled a face, unsure. 'Mum? Dad?'

I rolled my eyes.

'Sounds okay to me,' Dad said. 'I *think* I've seen it used in Scrabble before.'

'Hmm,' Mum mused, and tapped her chin with her forefinger. 'Me too.'

'Oh, for Pete's sake,' I hissed. 'You're all just scared of her.'

Laura was staring straight at me, her lips pursed together, fighting a smile.

'Fiiiiine,' I said, laughing a little. '*You* win.'

Mum was laughing too. She wrinkled her nose at me.

'So competitive.'

We'd been goading and teasing each other all morning. It was fun and familiar and all of us were revelling in it, Mum especially. She looked like the cat that got the cream. The five of us, back together again, laughing and sharing. This was what made her happy. This was what fuelled and empowered her. With all the pieces of the jigsaw now in place, the picture was clear: the battle was on and *could* be won. We all felt it and we all believed it.

'I've got to go,' Dad announced, suddenly.

Panic flashed across Mum's face. Dad smiled at her.

'Don't worry kiddo,' he soothed. 'I'll be back tomorrow, and *this* time, I'll be back for good.'

Mum's eyes moistened.

'Just gotta sort a few things,' he reassured her. 'The girls will look after you and I'll be back before you can blink.'

Mum nodded weakly. Dad leaned in to kiss her and stood up to leave, hugging us all in turn before marching out of the room.

Mum had been gone for well over two hours. They said she'd be back within the hour. Something must be wrong. I looked up at the clock for the millionth time. Where was she? A female nurse was walking towards me.

'Your mum's on her way back from theatre,' she informed me, while pulling the swing partition to one side to make way for Mum's bed. 'She's a little weepy,' she warned, 'but everything's okay.'

Weepy? Why was she weepy? I stood up and craned my neck around the ward wall, desperate to see her. I didn't have to wait long. The sight of her broke my heart. She was wrapped up tight in white hospital sheets, her head the only part of her visible. Tears were streaming down her face and her mouth was curled in a painful grimace. I clutched at my chest.

'There, there, Sally,' one of the nurses was saying. 'It's all over now, you're back in your room.'

Another nurse was walking around Mum's bed, locking the wheels into place.

'Excuse me,' I said quietly to her. 'Why is my mum so distraught? She was fine when she left.'

The nurse walked over to me and placed a comforting hand on my arm.

'It took a while to get the line in,' she explained, in a hushed and gentle tone. 'The doctor had to try twice.' The nurse smiled at me sweetly, 'Your mum just got a bit worked up, but she's okay.'

I took a couple of deep breaths, relieved that it wasn't something worse. I looked at the right side of Mum's neck where the line had been inserted and winced. It was bloody and bruised.

'It looks worse than it is,' the nurse reassured me. 'She's had a lot of pain relief.'

Ray was back in the room, after a trip to the loo, and staring at Mum in horror.

'What's wrong?' she demanded, colour draining from her face.

'It's okay,' I replied. 'Mum's fine,' I looked over at the nurse for back up. 'She's just a little overwhelmed.'

Ray scrunched up her face, dissatisfied.

'Honestly,' the nurse insisted. 'She's absolutely fine, please don't worry.'

The other nurse had pulled up a chair next to Mum's bed and was continuing to soothe her.

'There, there,' she whispered calmly, while stroking her head.

It seemed to be working; within minutes Mum was asleep. The nurse tiptoed away from the bed and turned towards me holding a paper cup.

'If she's in pain when she wakes, give her these.'

I peered into the cup. It contained four pills. 'And,' the nurse continued, 'make sure she drinks plenty of water. She needs to keep her fluids up.'

I nodded, 'Will do,' I assured her. 'Thank you.'

The nurses left and Ray and I quietly settled into our usual bedside positions. We had no idea how long she'd be asleep. She looked so peaceful. It was a relief to see her out of pain. I reached for a magazine – we'd bought a load earlier that morning from the hospital shop – and gratefully escaped into the lives of others.

Mum's chemo had arrived and was being carefully unwrapped by a short, curvy nurse called Claire, and placed on a tray on Mum's bed. She was wearing a thick blue gown and bright blue gloves and was sweating profusely. She pulled at her neckline with a grimace.

'I don't know why they have to make these gowns so tight. I can barely breathe!'

Mum pulled a face.

'You poor thing – '

'Now don't you go apologising,' Claire interrupted. 'This is nothing compared to what you've been through.' She pulled again at the restrictive neckline, 'but I will be having words.'

'And so you should,' I concurred. 'It's clearly getting in your way.'

Claire wiped her forehead with the back of her hand.

'They cost a bomb,' she said. '*And,*' she motioned for us to come closer, 'we don't even need 'em!'

I raised my eyebrows at her.

'We don't. The gloves give us all the protection we need.' Claire picked up one of three bags of drugs on the tray, flipped it over and inspected the back of it.

'But I'm just a nurse,' she shrugged theatrically. 'What do I know?'

I smiled at her. Her light-hearted approach to the severity of the task in hand was a welcome distraction and really helped to relax us. I wanted to reward her, so I took an interest.

'Have you been a nurse long?'

She placed a hand on her hip and thought it over.

'About twenty-odd years.'

'Wow,' said Ray.

Claire winked at her. 'I've given my age away now, haven't I?'

I was keen to find out more.

'Do you still enjoy it?'

'Mostly,' she admitted. 'But there's a lot of paperwork now, much less hands-on care.'

'Must be frustrating,' Mum sympathised.

'Certainly is,' Claire agreed. 'But I still get to nurse occasionally and meeting and helping lovely folk like you makes it all worthwhile.

She had us all smiling and welling up.

'Now, now,' she warned, in her broad Devonshire drool. 'Don't be doing that, or you'll set *me* off and I'll muddle up the drugs!'

Mum's eyes widened in alarm.

'Don't panic,' Claire chuckled. 'It's only happened once or twice.'

She took another swipe of her brow and looked at us all one by one. 'Ready?' she asked.

Mum nodded and a tear rolled slowly down her left cheek. I grabbed her hand and squeezed it.

'Perhaps we should encourage the chemo,' suggested Ray. 'Help it on its way.'

Mum let out a little laugh.

'I'm serious!' Ray insisted. 'Everybody hold hands. C'mon, c'mon. Excellent! Now, close your eyes and repeat after me: come on chemo, come on chemo, come on chemo.'

Hope flooded through me. 'Come on chemo, come on chemo ...' I repeated Ray's simple mantra over and over with all the passion I could muster.

It was an episode of *Friends* we'd seen countless times, but it was easy watching and could always be relied upon for a good giggle.

'Why does everyone think Rachel's the prettiest of all the girls in *Friends*?' I asked, genuinely baffled. Jennifer Aniston's universal appeal made little sense to me. Yes, she was attractive, but so too were Lisa Kudrow and Courteney Cox, more so, in my opinion.

'Her looks won't last,' Mum remarked. 'She hasn't got the bone structure.'

'I think she's cute,' Ray said. 'That's her appeal; girl next door.'

I considered this for a moment. Ray had got it in one. Jennifer Aniston was real and relatable. Courteney Cox, on the other hand, with her angular and symmetrical features, was a little too perfect, intimidating and unattainable.

'Look at Kate Moss,' said Ray. 'She's got exquisite bone

structure, but no man I know is that fussed on her. It's the women who find her attractive, who yearn to look like her.'

'True,' I agreed. 'Not that I'd mind looking like any of them, and I especially wouldn't mind Jennifer Aniston's boobs.'

'There's nothing wrong with your pretty little breasts, Kate-kins,' Mum smiled. 'Big boobs are a bloody nuisance.'

God love her. The woes of the busty woman – Mum could write a sermon on the subject. I knew every downside. They'd been pointed out to me my entire life.

'Be thankful you will never have to spend a fortune on these overpriced contraptions,' she'd say, while out shopping for bras with my well-endowed sisters. And when it was hot –

'I'd *love* to able to wear cute strappy summer tops like you Kate-kins. You're *so* lucky.'

It was all meant to placate me, but I could never be convinced, and like boob-less teens the world over, I tried everything I could think of to inflate them. I needn't have worried, I quickly realised that men didn't really care all that much. And as I got older, I learnt to appreciate the upsides. I'd certainly love for them to be a little bigger – Jennifer Aniston bigger – but they were what they were, and Chris enjoyed them. And at the end of the day, that was all that really mattered.

'You still don't really know how beautiful you are, do you?'

Mum was eyeing me with a curious expression.

'Claire was asking me all sorts of questions about you all when you both went to lunch,' Mum continued. 'She said she thought you were lovely looking girls, but that *you* were the most striking.'

'What?!' I scoffed, 'pah-*lease*!'

Mum shrugged her shoulders.

'She honestly couldn't believe it when I told her that you considered yourself to be the ugly sister.'

It was true, I did, and I always had. The three of us looked nothing alike. Feature for feature we were completely different. The similarities were there – big eyes, thick hair, strong chins – but they certainly didn't jump out at you. Laura had this ridiculously tiny ski-slope nose. God knows where she got it from. I, on the other hand, had what Mum called a strong and handsome nose. It wasn't big, but it wasn't small – something indescribably in-between – and I'd always disliked it. As well as her dainty, Disney nose, Laura had a perfectly proportioned figure, a real-life Barbie doll. I, on the other hand, was stick thin and boyish. Laura possessed a ballerina-type poise and grace, and oozed femininity.

I first truly noticed and marvelled at her appearance when I was twelve years old. It was a Saturday. We were both playing at a piano festival and were running late. Laura – fourteen and blooming–– was taking *forever* getting ready, and when she finally emerged the transformation was jaw dropping.

My gawky elder sister was a girl no more. She looked just like Jessica Rabbit. I looked down at my childish denim skirt, white tights and black patent slip-ons and quickly stepped aside, out of view, embarrassed. I would just have to play my stupid white tights off, I told myself; no one would see me otherwise. It was a moment that has stayed with me and had life-changing ramifications. From that day on I practised the piano daily and for hours on end. If I couldn't compete physically, I would wow musically. And I did, winning praise and trophies over and over, passing grade eight at just fourteen years of age. I became known as the talented sister, the achiever. But in truth, despite all the accolades, I yearned to be the 'beautiful' sister and would have traded my talent for knock-out looks in a heartbeat. It just seemed easier.

It was Ray, not me, who was relentlessly pursued by hotel staff and horny young holidaymakers during our second family holiday to Turkey. I was sixteen, she was fourteen. The eighteen-year-old son of the hotel owner was besotted with her. I was crushed and couldn't be consoled.

'Forget these silly foreign boys,' Mum would say. 'Your day will come.'

And she was right. It did. But the damage had been done. I'd brush off male advances with cold, mistrusting stares, scuppering chance after chance. They were either desperate or had been put up to it. No other explanation was possible, not to me anyway. Mum said, 'I was my own worst enemy' and as usual, she was right.

'Do you really believe that?'

Ray was looking at me, intently.

'What?' I replied.

'That you're the ugly sister?'

I shrugged my shoulders. Ray shook her head.

'Ridiculous!'

'Do you really believe that you're fat and less intelligent than me?' I cocked my head to one side, challenging her. Ray looked down at her hands, unsure.

'We all have our hang-ups, Ray, and we always want what we haven't got.'

Mum was nodding.

'Very true,' she agreed. 'I've always wanted to be taller and to be less booby. Well,' she giggled, looking down at her chest. 'I got my wish there.'

Ray and I laughed along with her.

'Ray's misplaced belief,' Mum continued, 'that she's fat and stupid is as preposterous as *your* belief Kate-kins that you're not as attractive as your sisters. But,' she sighed, 'neither of you will be told.'

It really was all rather ridiculous. In the greater scheme of things what did it matter? These deep-rooted demons we all carried around with us were mostly of our own making and just got in the way. I looked at Ray and Mum with love and affection. This moment – right here, right now – *this* was all that mattered.

CHAPTER 8

ONWARDS AND UPWARDS

The kitchen smelled divine. Chris had arrived for a one-night stay a couple of hours ago and was in the kitchen cooking a chicken curry. I hadn't seen him in over a week but in truth it felt a lot longer; so much had happened. I'd raced back from the hospital, happy to leave Ray and Dad to it, and stood by the front door awaiting his arrival like an overexcited puppy.

'How much longer?' I whined mounting a stool at the breakfast bar. 'I'm starving and it smells *so* good!'

'Couple more minutes,' Chris replied. 'Why don't you sort the drinks?'

I hopped off the stool and headed for the fridge. 'I'm having white,' I informed him. 'What do you want?' I opened the door and retrieved the wine box.

'White sounds good,' said Chris.

I filled up two glasses and returned to the breakfast bar, handing Chris one of the glasses. He clinked my glass and took a grateful glug.

'Good?' I asked.

Chris nodded.

'Very!' He replied and put down the glass to serve.

I wolfed down the meal, barely chewing. I couldn't help myself; it was the best thing I'd eaten in ages. I pictured Dad and Ray at the hospital canteen and felt a pang of guilt.

'Bloody hell!' Chris laughed. 'You polished that off good and quick. Nice?'

I looked down at my empty plate, sad it had all gone.

'You have no idea,' I replied, taking my forefinger and scooping up the last scrap of sauce. 'Fish and chips are as good as it gets around here.'

Chris frowned.

'Seriously?' he asked, soft and concerned. 'That's all you're eating?'

I'd worried him. He always got tetchy if he thought I wasn't eating properly. My cooking skills, or lack of, had long amused and baffled him.

'But your mum's a great cook,' he'd say. 'Did you not learn *anything*?'

No, I'd say, Mum didn't teach me or my sisters *anything*. This answer seemed to trouble him.

'Why not?' he'd ask. It was a question for which I had no reply.

The truth is I didn't *know* why and until Chris quizzed me about it, I'd never really given it much thought. Our presence in the kitchen, when we were kids, seemed to agitate her, so when Mum cooked, we left her to it. The only food we ever made for ourselves were sandwiches, cheese on toast etc. And even during these most basic of culinary tasks she'd make a big show of following us around and wiping away non-existent breadcrumbs. She wasn't exactly what you'd call 'supportive' of our efforts *away* from home either. Dishes prepared and brought back from Home Economics classes at school were panned and dumped with very few exceptions. Due to a lack of direction, skill and interest, most of my dishes – including an apple pie without apples – (yes, really), were inedible; a place on a plate denied. Luckily for me, Chris was a *great* cook and subsequently took on the bulk of the meals. But over the last year I'd been experimenting and as a result was starting to improve.

'No,' I lied. 'Fish and chips isn't *all* we eat; I'm cooking when I can.' I wasn't, but *I planned to*, which was pretty much the same thing.

'Good,' said Chris, visibly relaxing.

He sloped off his stool, walked round to my side of the bar and reached out both arms for a hug. I stood up, folded my arms around his waist and rested my head on his chest. I closed my eyes, savouring the moment.

'If you're worried,' I said, seconds later, 'you should stay and cook for me every day …' I looked up and grinned. Chris took my face in his hands.

'I would if I could.'

I batted my eyelashes, 'Please?'

Chris kissed the tip of my nose and smiled.

'I've missed you.'

'I've missed you too.' I threw my arms around his big, strong neck. 'Ray will be back soon,' I said, 'so how about …' I let the words hang there, suggestively.

'How about, what?' he teased.

I narrowed my eyes. 'You know what!'

Leaning in, he cocked his head to one side, his eyes sparkling with mischief.

'Do I?'

'It might be the only chance we get.'

'Well,' he said, 'when you put it like that, how in the world can I refuse?'

I glanced up at the clock on the microwave: 4.30 pm. Ray would be back within the hour. It was now or never. I grabbed Chris' hand and led him quickly upstairs.

With Dad now staying at the cottage permanently the three of us quickly settled into a routine. Ray and I spent the morning with Mum. Then Dad would join us from midday, and Ray and I would head off home about five, leaving the two of them alone. Ray had taken to daily jogs with the dogs and I, feeling bad about the little white lie I'd told, had stocked up on supplies and cooked our evening meals.

Dad had got to the root of the boiler problem – damp coal apparently – and the house was now heated, morning, noon and night. Not that it was such a concern now as Britain was basking in a mini heatwave. I'd dance about to Mum's iPod while I prepared dinner and sit outside with Ray, sipping wine, until the sun went down. We saw Laura every three or four days, always between eight in the morning and one in the afternoon.

Dad would come into the hospital early when Laura was about so that we could all be together. Scrabble continued, but the game we played and enjoyed the most, was a simple card game from our childhood: 'Uno'. It was seriously addictive; we could play it for hours.

We filled our days with love and laughter. So much so that it was becoming all too easy to forget *why* we were all here. The sudden arrival of a nurse or a doctor would always jolt us back to reality. They only ever turned up if something was wrong. If Mum's temperature spiked above thirty-seven a doctor would appear, roughly half an hour or so later, and conduct an examination.

'Does it hurt if I press here?' They'd ask, or 'Feeling sick at all?'

Mum's response was nearly always, no. And so, to bring down her temperature, the Doctor would prescribe paracetamol or a course of antibiotics. This would then be added to Mum's ever-increasing medical file, now bigger and possibly more lethal than the notorious and infamous Iraq Dossier.

'Mum?' Laura said.

I shifted my gaze from the female doctor tending to Mum, to Laura who was suddenly sitting very straight in her chair, looking curiously triumphant.

'When did you last have a poo?'

Unfazed by Laura's outburst, Mum narrowed her eyes slightly and puckered her lips in contemplation.

'Yesterday morning, I think. Why?'

Laura's eyes glistened with glory.

'I think that's why you have a temperature!'

Mum and I exchanged a bewildered glance.

'I've noticed,' Laura continued, 'that if you've not gone for a while, your temperature goes up.'

Mum raised one of her barely there eyebrows.

'Seriously,' said Laura, 'it happens every time!'

She threw a quick glance at me and then back at Mum before turning her head towards the Doctor who was busy scribbling in Mum's file.

'Well?' Laura pressed. 'What do you think?'

Her eyes were as big as saucers. My lips twitched, fighting the urge to smile. Poor Doctor, her opinion was irrelevant really – Laura's mind was made up; she didn't need her theory validated. Still, she smiled at the Doctor angelically. The room was silent with anticipation.

'Uhmm,' the doctor said shifting her weight from one foot to the other. 'It's an interesting idea.'

Typical doctor – diplomatic, detached, overly cautious.

'To be honest,' she ventured, 'it's not something I've ever really noticed or been made aware of before in other patients, but that's not to say it might not be true in your mum's case. Establishing the cause is tricky. It would be unwise not to administer antibiotics because your mum is neutropenic and as a result more susceptible to infection. If we don't get on top of a potential infection, it becomes harder to treat.' A slight pause and then a patronising smile. 'I'm not ruling your theory out, but I'm afraid we can't simply ignore it – the risks are too great.'

Laura, still wide eyed and smiling, considered the Doctor's response. It was a second or two before she spoke.

'I *know* you can't ignore it and I'm not asking you to. It's just a theory; an observation.' Laura leaned in closer to Mum, grabbed one of her hands and grinned. 'Let's see what happens when you next go to the loo.'

Mum chuckled; it warmed my heart, it always did. 'The nurse will be in soon.' The Doctor said matter-of-factly and turned to leave. Once she was out of earshot, we dissolved into giggles.

'What did I miss?'

Ray bounced into the room clutching her tenth cup of tea of the day. Mum looked straight at her, amused.

'Laura thinks I've got a temperature because I can't crap!'

That set us all off again.

An hour later we'd all but forgotten the threat from the nurse earlier to fetch the dietician. So when a tall woman with fine, red hair and a long, narrow face quietly rapped on the door of Mum's room, we all looked up from our conversation slightly startled. We shot curious glances at each other. Who was she? We knew all the consultants and she couldn't possibly be a nurse, the beige shirt-like overall she was wearing told us that. So, who the hell was she?

'Hello,' she said sweetly.

'Hi,' we all replied in mumbled unison. No need to be over friendly, best keep it casual until we knew *why* she was here and *what* she wanted. We were way less trusting of medical personnel these days. We all sat up a little straighter, steeling ourselves, like meerkats, and watched as she tentatively tore off a pink plastic apron from the roll beside the door.

It took her a while to figure it out and fasten it around her neck and waist. A clue. We were all experts with that bloody apron roll because we were in and out of Mum's room all day long. This woman, whoever she was, clearly didn't make a habit of visiting patients, well, not neutropenic patients anyway. This was made clearer still by her miserable attempt at putting on a pair of blue latex gloves. I ran a hand through my hair, glanced over at Mum and rolled my eyeballs in mock despair. Ray bit her lip fighting back a giggle and looked towards our unexpected visitor. Gloves finally on, the woman tucked a stray strand of hair behind her ear and stepped nervously into the room. I squinted at the name badge pinned to her shirt, but it was obscured by the apron and too small to make out. Oh well, I'd find out soon enough.

'Hello,' she said again stopping at the end of Mum's bed. 'Sorry for the intrusion, my name's Jane. I'm a dietician.'

Ah, of course! I slumped back into my chair; nothing to worry about. Ray and Mum smiled warmly, and Laura leaned forward, as she always did when someone medical entered the room, resting her elbows on Mum's bed and her face in her hands. Jane smoothed out her apron and looked only at Mum.

'I've come to see you because the doctors are concerned about your weight. They'd all be a lot happier if you were eating and drinking a bit more.'

'Would they?' Mum scoffed. 'If *they* were stuck in here and served up tasteless, vile slop day after day, *they'd* lose weight too.'

Quiet giggles rippled through the room. A full-on rant was coming, no doubt about it!

'Have you seen what they give us?! It's revolting! And the smell ...' Mum grimaced, purely for effect, and pushed herself up from her elbows, sitting up unsupported.

'It's an outrage. I've no immune system – the drugs I've had have completely wiped it out! You'd think nutritional food would be a necessity, help keep my strength up, but no, I'm served shitty, stinky bowls of crap every goddamned day.'

Jane, who had remained perfectly still, hands clasped tightly together behind her back, opened her mouth slightly to interject but was quickly silenced by Mum, who was on a roll.

'The food from the restaurant is poor too, isn't it girls?' Mum looked at us one by one, brown eyes bulging. We all nodded obligingly. 'What was it I had the other day, Kate? That beige coloured dish?'

I racked my brain searching for the memory. 'Uhmm ...' Crap! What was it? Mum needed me, she needed back-up; I couldn't fail her. Think, Kate, think!

'It was ...' Shit! What the bloody hell was it?!

And then I remembered. 'Urgh, yeah, it was *awful*!' I looked at Jane with exaggerated disgust. 'It was advertised as fish pie with vegetables but what *actually* arrived was dry, tired looking pieces of salmon in a beige sauce with hard bits of carrot in it.' I shuddered at the memory. 'Gross. Really, *really* unappetising.' I shifted my gaze from Jane to Mum who nodded approvingly.

'So,' Mum continued, 'mystery solved. I've lost weight because the food here is inedible.'

Satisfied, Mum leaned back on her pillows and stared at Jane, signalling for her to respond. Poor woman, she looked a bit shell-shocked. Mum's little rant was clearly not what she had expected. She probably had a speech planned, one she rattled out for all underweight patients. Mum's tirade had clearly knocked her off course.

'Okay,' Jane said finally, nodding her head a few times and smiling shyly. 'What to do then?' She pondered, tapping a long pale finger on her pointy chin. 'You've lost over half a stone in under a week, and we can't let it dip any further. Unfortunately, I can't get the chef at the restaurant here to make you up something else and the food from the trolley is ferried over from Swansea – '

'What?' cried Mum, wide-eyed in disbelief. She'd propped herself back up onto her elbows, her jaw slightly ajar. 'The food is ferried over from *Swansea*?'

'Yes,' Jane replied, matter-of-factly. 'That's where the food is made. It's supplied to the hospital by a catering company who specialise in designing food that best meets the nutritional needs of patients. Patients like you.'

Mum snorted. 'But it's awful! It has zero substance and always looks anaemic. You couldn't *pay* someone to eat it! Have you seen it?'

'No,' Jane admitted. 'But it can't be that bad.'

Mum was laughing now, clearly enjoying herself.

'Trust me, it's bad. Really, *really* bad.' She shook her head. 'Ferried over from Swansea … unbelievable.'

Jane's freckled cheeks flushed. Mum noticed too and looked a little guilty.

'I'm sorry,' she offered, 'it's not your fault.'

'No, no,' Jane said, waving her hands frantically in front of her. '*Please* don't apologise. It's good to know what you think about the food here. We're always trying to find ways to improve it.' A smile played around the corners of Jane's lips. 'And by the sounds of it, we've got a lot to improve upon.'

A breakthrough, we all sensed it. Jane looked a little more relaxed, her shoulders had dropped, her face less severe, soft even. She curled her long fingers around the steel railing at the end of Mum's bed.

'So,' she began, 'we need to get your weight up. The question is, how? There are several things we can try,' Jane continued and rattled off a list of options.

'Cereal bars, the ones with lots of oats in. You can have as many of those as you like. Biscuits are also good, as is chocolate. Fruit. Wrapped fruit – including bananas – though make sure they're not bruised. Boxes of raisins, tinned fruit – all supermarkets stock such things, and here at the hospital we can give you protein shakes – '

'Urgh,' Mum shuddered.

Jane looked at her inquisitively.

'Can't tolerate milk,' Mum said. 'Makes me feel sick, always has.'

'We could always dilute it,' suggested Jane. 'Take the edge off?' Mum pulled a face.

'Or not,' Jane laughed. 'No big deal, they're not essential. It wouldn't hurt to try though – shakes are a really easy way to build up bulk.'

Hmmm, this was not a fight the dietician was likely to win. Dairy was pretty much a no-go area for Mum, though, if it could help, I knew Mum would consider it. Stubborn, yes. Stupid, no.

'I always knew chocolate was good for you.'

All heads turned to Laura who was grinning from ear to ear.

'Like you need an excuse!' I retorted, chuckling.

'Mmmm ...' Laura's eyes glazed over, 'chocolate ...'

'How are you not the size of a house?' I teased.

Laura grabbed her belly with both hands and wiggled it up and down.

'What do you call this?'

'Baby fat,' I replied quickly.

'Some of it, yes, but the rest of it is chocolate.'

We both giggled.

'And what's more,' Laura continued. 'I don't care!'

Mum and Ray were chuckling now, Jane too.

'So,' said Mum, brushing away a happy tear. 'Which one of you is going to get me some sugary treats?'

We all jumped at the chance, answering with frantic nods and hand-raises. An opportunity to do something useful! This didn't happen very often.

'Looks like you're being well cared for,' observed Jane.

Mum locked eyes with all three of us and we all beamed back at her. Jane smiled and started edging backwards towards the door, peeling off her gloves.

'I'll tell the nurses we've talked about the possibility of protein shakes,' both gloves were now off and in the bin. 'So, if you want to try one, just let them know. Okay?'

Mum nodded. 'Don't hold your breath,' she said.

Jane smiled and lightly yanked at her apron. It would take more than that to remove it. The plastic was surprisingly tough. She tugged at it again, harder this time.

'I'll pop in and see you in a few days' time,' she said. 'See how you're getting on.'

Another tug. Nothing. The apron was still fixed firmly in place. Visibly annoyed now, though trying desperately hard not to show it, Jane ripped at the apron with both hands. It worked. The apron was off. A little triumphant smile crept across her lips. Such a small victory, but a victory, nonetheless. She looked up and caught my eye. I smiled knowingly. Embarrassed, Jane relocated the bin, discarded the tattered remnants of the apron and walked quickly away.

CHAPTER 9

OOPS!

Ray unlocked the back door to Mum's cottage and froze.

'Oh. My. God!'

I raced down the steps having parked the car after another long day at the hospital and peered over her shoulder into the kitchen. My eyes nearly popped out of their sockets.

'What the hell?!' I took a couple of steps back and covered my face with my hand attempting to mask the smell. Ray spun round, doubled over and gagged. I inched back to the door for a second look. Pinching my nose, I scanned the room.

'I bet it was Wilf.' Ray was standing beside me, staring at the kitchen floor in disbelief. 'He was a bit sad this morning, barely touched his breakfast.'

I locked eyes with her, astonished.

'Well, where the bloody hell did all that come from then? I've never *seen* so much shit!'

Ray giggled and shook her head.

'He must have eaten something bad yesterday, something that didn't agree with him.'

'Something bad?' I twisted my face in disgust. 'Something evil, more like.'

Ray stepped cautiously into the room.

'It's absolutely everywhere,' she said. 'It's going to take forever to clean.'

I ran a hand through my hair and sighed. She was right, it would take hours! The kitchen cabinets had even got a spraying. I'd never seen anything like it, well, except in a cow field.

'Where is he?' Ray pondered, looking around.

'Probably in hiding,' I replied, 'ashamed.'

'Wilf?' Ray yelled. 'Wilf?'

We walked through the dining room and into the lounge and found him cowering and shivering in the corner, his tail limply wagging. We burst out laughing.

'It's okay Wilf,' Ray said quietly, 'we're not mad.'

I folded my arms across my chest.

'Yes, we bloomin' well are!'

Ray dropped to her knees and embraced him.

'No, we're not,' she giggled. 'Don't listen to mean old Gus.'

'Check his arse,' I instructed.

Picking up his tail, she wrinkled her nose, jerked her head back and retched.

It made me laugh. 'Bad?'

'Really, *really* bad,' she grimaced.

Wilf looked at us both, apologetically. I rolled my eyes. Dogs.

Back in the kitchen Ray handed me a pair of rubber gloves, filled a bucket with hot water and bleach and reached into the cabinet below the sink for kitchen towel and bin bags.

Something else caught my eye.

'Hand me one of those would you?'

She looked up at me, puzzled. I pointed at a small fabric bag.

'A clothes peg,' I said.

Ray furrowed her brow.

'For the smell.'

'Ahh,' she smiled. 'Good idea!'

Turns out it *wasn't* such a good idea. The pegs were made of plastic and clung on like crab claws; the pain was excruciating. We quickly gave up on them and got through it by breathing through our mouths instead.

Once we'd removed all the crap and washed the floors we headed outside to deal with Wilf, or more specifically, Wilf's butt. Ray dragged him outside by his collar and made me sit with him while she located a comb and some scissors. She quickly returned and sat down on the patio, cross-legged in front of him. This was her domain.

'Turn him round Gus and straddle him to keep him still.'

I did as I was told.

'Whoa!' Ray laughed. 'Not so close!'

Ray and Wilf were face to butt.

'Lift his tail so that I can get a good look.'

I picked up the tip of his tail and held it aloft. Ray looked up at me and grimaced.

'There's so much hair!'

Wilf tried to creep forward.

'Oh no you don't!' I warned him and steered him back towards Ray.

She started snipping at his backside, carefully cutting away clumps of crusty poo.

'Shit!' she said.

Wilf yelped and tried to escape. I looked at Ray with alarm and tightened my grip around Wilf's ribcage.

'What?' I asked.

'I think I just cut him,' she replied. 'It's impossible to see his butt with all this hair!'

Ten minutes later Ray announced that she was done.

'I think I've got it all,' she said, standing up to stretch.

I moved Wilf's tail to one side and had a quick peek.

'Yep,' I agreed. 'Still stinks though. Should probably hose him down.'

'Or,' she suggested, 'we just wipe his arse with a damp dishcloth?'

I walked into the kitchen and retrieved the bucket of hot water and bleach that we'd used for cleaning the floor.

'Bleach?' Ray queried when I placed the bucket down beside her.

I shrugged my shoulders and resumed my position. Ray dunked the dishcloth into the bucket and started scrubbing. Wilf wasn't keen, his back legs were trembling, and he kept trying to sit. I had to keep yanking him back up by his tail.

'There,' said Ray, a short while later. 'All done.'

I released my grip and set Wilf free.

By the time we'd sorted out Wilf's shit explosion it was close to six-thirty and my enthusiasm for the mini roast dinner I had planned to cook had well and truly waned. I mulled it over and decided to press on. The reward would be worth the effort.

'Where does Mum keep her baking trays?' I asked Ray, who was squatting in front of the fire, chucking in a handful of coal.

'In the cupboard to the right of the sink,' she replied.

I bent down and opened the door. Ray was right; a couple of baking trays were tightly wedged under a large burnt orange Le Creuset saucepan. Retrospectively, what I should have done next was remove the saucepan, place it on the kitchen counter and gone back for the baking tray. What I *actually* did was yank the baking tray from *underneath* the saucepan, sending it tumbling out of the cabinet onto my foot. I screamed and reached for my foot. The pain was overwhelming. Ray spun round to face me.

'Gus?'

Her face was a blur. The floor tilted below me. I scrambled for the stool underneath the kitchen worktop, but I couldn't get to it. I felt sick; little bright white lights were jumping about in front of my eyes. I made one last attempt to grab the stool, but I lost my footing, and everything went dark.

I was on the floor. Why was I on the floor? Ray was crouched over me, her eyes wide with concern. She was saying something, but I couldn't hear her. My head felt fuzzy, and my chin hurt. Why was I on the floor? And why was I so hot? Was my foot on fire? I tore at my cardigan and pulled off my T-shirt. My chin was throbbing, and I was sweating. Ray was trying to haul me up into a sitting position.

'What's going on?' I heard myself ask.

'You blacked out,' replied Ray, 'and hit your chin on the worktop.'

'What?'

'You blacked out and – '

But I wasn't listening. I couldn't feel my left arm. It was numb.

'Ray,' I complained, 'I can't feel my left arm.'

I tried to wiggle my fingers. They wouldn't move.

'Ray?'

I looked at my hand in horror.

'Don't panic,' said Ray. 'You're just panicking, calm down.'

I looked down at my black vest top. It was drenched. I was suddenly aware of my foot. It was throbbing, but it was cold. Ray was pressing an ice cube to it. When had she got that? I stared at it; it was bright red. Ray was staring at me with renewed alarm.

'Your lips have turned white.'

Wrapping her arms around me, she pulled me up into Mum's beloved rocking chair by the fire. Then she shifted the stool from out underneath the worktop and rested my foot on it.

My arm: I still couldn't feel it. I made another attempt to wiggle my fingers. Ray picked up the phone and dialled. Seconds later she handed me the phone.

'It's a nurse,' Ray informed me. 'She wants to ask you a few questions.'

My arm started tingling.

'Hello?'

I answered all the nurse's questions and breathed a sigh of relief; I'd be fine. The pain from my foot had sent my body into shock. My body had shut down to protect me. I was now having an anxiety attack and that's why I couldn't feel my arm; the feeling would come back. Phew. Calmed by the nurse's reassuring words, I started to relax. Ray handed me a tea towel – she'd wrapped some ice cubes in it and told me to press it against my chin. I looked at my foot. It was changing colour. Deep purple marks appeared just below my little toe. This must have been where the pot had landed.

'You scared me for a moment,' Ray said, inspecting my foot.

'I scared myself!' I replied and we both laughed.

'You should try standing on it.'

I stood up on my right leg, steading myself by holding onto the wall, and lowered my left foot to the floor. I tried to put some pressure on it, but a sharp pain shot through me and I quickly retracted my foot and slumped back into the chair. Great – what use was I if I couldn't bloody drive? I wondered if I'd broken a bone. Ray giggled.

'If only you could see yourself!'

Reaching for her mobile, she took a picture and showed it to me. Good God. My chin had doubled in size!

'I look like Desperate Dan!'

She took another snap, this time of my foot.

'Mum's gonna love this!'

Shaking my head in disbelief, I smiled. What unnecessary drama. I looked over at the pile of vegetables on the chopping board and then at the baking tray and finally at the Le Creuset saucepan on the floor. The mini roast would have to wait. Ray followed my gaze.

'Fish and chips?' She suggested, and we laughed until it hurt.

'You did *what*?!'

Mum's eyes widened in horror.

'We wiped Wilf's arse with bleach,' I said again, but slightly slower.

Mum shook her head, stunned.

'You don't wipe a dog's arse with bleach!' She raised her eyes to the heavens. 'Good God girls!'

A smile was dancing around Dad's lips.

'Poor Wilf,' he said. 'He's probably got a very sore backside.'

Ray and I giggled.

'He seems okay,' said Ray, sheepishly. Dad started laughing which set us all off, including Mum.

'You're supposed to be good with animals,' she said to Ray, once she'd got her laughter under control. 'You should've known better!'

'It was Gus' idea!' Ray blurted. I narrowed my eyes at her.

'Traitor!'

At that point a doctor breezed into the room.

'Good news!' She announced, clutching onto a freshly printed sheet of paper. 'Your blood count is *still* down!'

'Really?!' Mum asked, wide eyed and beaming.

'Yes,' the Doctor confirmed. 'You have the same number of white blood cells you had last week.'

I quietly clapped my hands together.

'We'll have to check your bone marrow, see what's happening there,' the doctor warned. 'But there's no doubt about it, the chemo has definitely had some sort of effect.'

I looked over at Mum. She was grinning from ear to ear, tears rolling silently down her cheeks.

'And what's more,' the doctor continued, 'if your count *remains* down, you might even be able to go home for a bit.'

My stomach did a little flip.

'That's excellent news,' Dad said smiling at Mum. 'Isn't it love?'

Mum nodded and reached for a tissue.

'We'll let you know for sure in a couple of days.' The doctor smiled and filed the piece of paper she was holding into Mum's medical folder. 'Any questions while I'm here?'

We all looked at each other and shook our heads. The Doctor nodded, smiled and left the room.

Just as I was about to start whooping and clapping along with the rest of my family, I was struck by an all too familiar cramping pain in my abdomen. I jumped up too quickly putting pressure on my wounded foot and let out a blood-curdling shriek. Everyone looked at me, concerned.

'It's okay,' I reassured them, closing my eyes to control the pain. Mum's brow crinkled with concern.

'I wish you'd get it looked at,' she said.

'No need,' I assured her. 'It's not broken, just a bit bruised.'

'You don't know that – '

'Yes, I do,' I snapped, unfairly, but I needed to get to a toilet.

'Okay, okay,' Mum said, holding her hands up in front of her face, defensively. 'But if it gets any worse, I'll have to insist.'

I nodded and hobbled out of the room.

The cramps were getting worse; they were coming in waves. I locked myself in the toilet cubicle and dropped my knickers. My heart sank. Blood.

CHAPTER 10

HOMECOMING

I flopped onto the sofa next to Ray, exhausted. We'd done it. The transformation was complete; Mum's house was dirt and dust free. I dropped my head onto Ray's shoulder.

'I hope she likes what we've done with the place.'

'She will,' said Ray. 'Especially the flowers, she'll love all the fresh flowers.'

I looked around the lounge, admiring our handiwork. A big purple Yankee candle was flickering on the shelf by the TV. It had been alight for about an hour, its lavender scent filling the room. I closed my eyes and inhaled.

The shrill of Mum's landline startled me awake. I'd drifted off. I never drift off. I looked over at Ray. She was sound asleep. The phone. I carefully got up and limped towards it.

'Hello,' I said, groggily. Silence. 'Hello?'

'Kate, it's Dad. Bad news.'

My stomach lurched into my chest.

'We've just had a visit from one of the consultants. Mum can still come home for the weekend, but it doesn't look good.'

I dropped like a stone onto the stool beside me.

'She has leukemic cells in her bone marrow. So, according to the consultant,' Dad stopped, cleared his throat, and quickly carried on, 'it's just a matter of time.'

I looked up to the ceiling and breathed in hard.

'What about her blood?' I asked.

Dad sighed.

'Still normal.'

Stupid consultant, why did he have to say anything? He knew Mum was coming home, why couldn't he just keep that information to himself? Let her enjoy a weekend in the sun with her family.

'How's Mum?' I asked, eventually.

Dad's voice broke.

'Not good.'

Crap.

'When will you be back?'

'Just packing up the last of her bits now,' Dad replied. 'So, about an hour?'

I said goodbye, hung up and dropped my head into my hands.

Ray and I stood awkwardly in the hallway awaiting Mum and Dad's return. I was angry, really angry, some homecoming. I'd be having words with that bloody consultant; he'd messed it all up. The bonnet of Dad's car slowly rolled into view. Ray flinched beside me. Standing in the hallway suddenly felt wrong. Or perhaps I just wanted to delay the inevitable. Either way I grabbed Ray's hand and dragged her into the kitchen.

'I think we should wait for Mum in here,' I said quickly, 'give her some space.'

The car door slammed. It sent a chill straight through me. The front door opened. Mum was inside. I bit my lip. Dad appeared. He was slowly walking in front of Mum, obscuring her from view. Our eyes locked. He stepped to one side and let go of Mum's hand.

'Home sweet home,' he said quietly.

Mum stood motionless in the doorway, frail and small. She caught my eye and quickly looked away. Her face suddenly crumpled, and her hands shot up to her face. Then a noise, unlike anything I'd ever heard. It was the sound of loss and torment. It kept on coming. Tears streamed down her face splashing onto the floor below. What to do? Rush over and comfort her? I tried to move but I was stuck, rooted to the spot, completely transfixed. Dad dipped his head onto his chest, completely at a loss. The crying eventually slowed and ten minutes or so later stopped altogether. She reached for Dad and said she wanted to sit in her rocking chair. He guided her towards it and sat in the chair opposite.

'Sorry girls,' Mum sniffed, while retrieving a tissue from her bag.

Ray and I shook our heads, furiously.

'Don't be sorry,' we said.

I searched Mum's face for clues. I desperately wanted her to talk to us, tell us what was going through her mind. Instead, she sat gazing sadly at the fire. We didn't push her; she'd talk in her own time. I filled the kettle and made a cup of tea. We drank in continued silence.

Eventually, Mum spoke. 'I like the rug.'

As part of our 'big clean' Ray and I had chucked out and replaced Mum's tired oatmeal rug with a brand new red one.

'We got it from Tavistock market,' I said.

Mum nodded and smiled up at me.

'Looks good.'

She cast her eye over the vase of lilies on the worktop.

'They're beautiful too.'

It was now or never. 'You know,' I began. 'It might not be as bad as it sounds. If the leukaemia is only in your bone marrow you might now be eligible for a transplant.'

Silence. I changed tack. 'It's a beautiful day, why don't we take your rocking chair outside, sit you under the tree?'

Dad nodded and squeezed Mum's hand.

'Sounds like a great idea. How 'bout it kiddo?'

Mum yawned, nodded and handed her empty mug to Ray requesting more. Dad got up and opened the back door letting in a shaft of sunlight. He turned back to Mum, helped her up and led her out into the garden.

A couple of hours in the sunshine worked wonders. Mum was smiling and chatting and seemed calm and relaxed. I, on the other hand, felt wretched. Anger raged within me. That stupid, thoughtless consultant; I could kill him! How *dare* he ruin our weekend. Mum hadn't been home with us all in forever! There was only one thing that would make me feel better: alcohol, and lots of it. I shot up out of my chair and marched towards the kitchen. Grabbing a glass, I filled it with cold, white wine and gulped it down. I slumped back against the fridge, exhilarated. It tasted so good! I picked up the wine box and re-joined my family at the table.

An hour later I was more than a little tipsy. I had downed glass after glass. The anger had dissipated but my guts were still churning. Every time I blinked, tiny tears would escape and roll silently down my cheeks. I fixed sunglasses to my face to hide them, but Mum was no fool.

'I see you,' she said quietly.

I turned to face her. She was smiling and reached out for my hand. I put down my wine glass, removed my shades and let the tears flow.

'I just –' I bit my lip and closed my eyes.

Mum squeezed my hand.

'I know.'

We stared at each other for a long time.

'It's bollocks!' I blurted out eventually. 'Big fat hairy bollocks!'

Ray laughed.

'Hear, hear!' she said, and topped up our glasses.

By sunset I was blissfully drunk and could have stayed outside looking up at the stars all night long. Mum was cold though, so we went inside and started a game of Scrabble. It didn't last long. I couldn't see straight and knocked the board off the table. We tried a game of cards instead, but I quickly put a stop to that too; I wasn't really interested. I wanted to talk to Mum, ask her questions. What was her favourite colour? Film? Book? I wanted to know *everything*. I started slurring my words and repeating my questions, but the wine kept flowing.

Dad wasn't amused.

'You've already asked that, Kate,' he said. And 'Don't you think you've had enough, Kate?' Nope. I grabbed the box in defiance. It was empty. Had I drank it all? The room started to spin. I felt a bit sick. Water. I needed water. I looked at my dad, bemused. He had two heads. I squinted at him. *Still* two heads. Water. I stumbled into the kitchen. I started to sway. Sleep. Perhaps a quick lie down. I spotted Wilf's bed, curled up and closed my eyes.

'Kate?'

'Gus?'

'Here she is.'

'Gus?'

I opened my eyes; Ray's blurred face was staring back at me.

'Come on,' she said, pulling me to my feet, 'you don't want to sleep here.'

I looked down at the dog's bed, confused. Why was I asleep in Wilf's bed? And why did I feel so dizzy?

'I'm gonna be sick,' I slurred.

Ray rushed me into the bathroom and positioned me by the toilet. Vomit exploded from my mouth in relentless waves. Ray crouched down next to me and held back my hair while I hugged the loo like a long-lost friend.

'I want to sick it all out,' I heard myself saying. 'It's all disgusting! It's got to come out. It's dirty, it's wrong!'

Oh God, would it ever end?! My chest was burning, and I was seeing spots. I wanted to die. Mum appeared in the doorway.

'How's she doing?'

Just swell, I wanted to say, but a fresh wave of vomit put a stop to that.

'She's getting there,' Ray replied. 'Can you get Dad to bring her up a glass of water?'

Mum nodded and left the room. Sod water, I thought, sleep was what I needed, and lots of it. I released my clasp from the toilet and carefully hauled myself to my feet.

'Steady,' Ray warned.

I shook her off and tentatively walked, by myself, towards my bedroom. Ten minutes later I was back in the bathroom. Eventually though, in the early hours, I was done. The room finally stopped spinning and sleep was mine.

I was dead. I was sure of it. There were hundreds of people stomping about inside my head and that isn't possible on Earth. My eyes were stuck together. I attempted to open them. Why was it so bright? Was I in heaven? I swallowed and winced. My throat felt tight and scratchy. I felt sick and hollow and ached all over. Perhaps I'd been in a fight? The pain in my head was intolerable, and it was getting worse. I lifted a heavy, shaky arm and rubbed my temples with my fingers. My stomach growled unapologetically. I clutched at it with my other hand. I could hear water running and muffled voices.

'Knock, knock.'

Someone was in the room. I squinted. Ray's face slowly came into view. Shit. It all came flooding back. I wasn't dead; I was hungover, horribly hungover. Ray started giggling.

'Not feeling so good?' she chirped.

Hysterical. I tried to respond, but nothing came out. My mouth was dry; my throat clogged.

'I'll get you some painkillers and some dry toast.'

I shuddered at the thought of it, but Ray was gone before I could protest. I wasn't comfortable lying down; perhaps I'd feel better if I sat up? I pushed both hands down on the bed and wriggled my body up the wall. I wasn't *sitting* exactly, but I was a bit more upright than before. I spotted a glass of water on the bedside table and reached for it. I took a couple of sips. Yuck. It was warm and tainted.

'Ah,' said Ray, a few minutes later, 'you're up!'

'Hardly,' I croaked.

'Here,' she said, holding out a plate, 'toast.'

'Thanks,' I mumbled grumpily, rubbing my head. 'Why didn't you stop me?'

Ray smiled.

'You were on a mission, Gus. It was obviously something you needed to do.'

Panic surged through me.

'Mum!' I cried. 'How is she?'

Ray handed me a couple of painkillers.

'Fine,' she replied. 'Absolutely fine. Soaking in the tub.'

I closed my eyes, relieved. Not that I could have done anything about it if she wasn't okay, not in this state. I was a crap daughter. A crap, thoughtless, useless daughter.

'Morning piss head!' Dad was smiling smugly at me from the doorway. He looked and sounded way too fresh and happy. 'How ya doing?'

I winced. Did he have to shout?!

'That bad, eh?'

Dad folded his arms across his chest.

'A cold, damp cloth for your head?' he suggested.

I looked up at him, a little surprised and nodded.

'I'll go get you one.'

Ray looked just as shocked as me.

'Dad, Florence Nightingale?' she said, disbelieving. 'Who knew?'

I sat slumped in my bed for most of the morning, but by eleven I'd had enough. I wanted to see Mum. I wobbled as I stood and gripped the wall for support. This was going to take a while. I peeled the cloth Dad had given me from my forehead and reached for my cardigan. I couldn't get my arms through; the sleeves were all twisted up. I rolled my eyes. Pushing my feet into my slippers, I shuffled into the bathroom and approached the mirror with caution. If I looked anywhere near as bad as I felt this wasn't going to be pretty. It wasn't. Never again, I said to myself, never a-fucking-gain. I brushed my teeth and made my way to the kitchen.

I could hear them all long before I saw them, but conversation immediately stopped as soon as I entered the room. Mum was sitting in her rocking chair, snuggled up by the fire in her dressing gown, clutching a cup of tea.

'Oh sweetheart,' she said softly, a smile fighting for acceptance at both corners of her mouth. 'Come and sit down.'

I plonked myself down onto the chair opposite. Dad and Ray were chuckling.

'I know, I know,' I said, smoothing down my hair. 'I look a fright.'

'Did the cloth help?' Dad asked, eagerly.

I nodded.

'Good,' he replied. 'I often find it helps when I've got a migraine.'

So *that's* how he came up with it. Ray and I shared a knowing look.

'I can do you some eggs?' Dad offered.

My face said it all.

'Too soon?'

I nodded.

'A shower's what she needs,' Mum said brightly.

This was a better idea, but then I remembered where I was: a shower at home, yes. Fannying about with that shit, unfriendly contraption upstairs? No.

'I haven't got the energy,' I said, sleepily.

'Could always hose you down outside,' Ray suggested. Mum looked at her in horror.

'You can't do that, she's not a dog!'

But it sounded like a great idea to me! I was keen, *really* keen.

'Let's do it!' I said, properly smiling for the first time that morning. 'It'll be like standing under a waterfall!'

Ray looked a little unsure.

'Really?' she checked, disbelieving, 'I was joking!'

'I'm not,' I insisted. 'It's a great idea!'

'Cool!' Ray beamed, rubbing her hands together. 'This is gonna be fun!' She hopped off the stool and opened the back door. Mum shook her head at me and laughed. I grinned back at her pleased that my misfortune was amusing her.

Back in my room I rummaged through my clothes for my swimming costume. I'd brought it with me thinking I might get a chance to do a few laps in the local pool. Five minutes later, I was *still* looking for it. I was knackered. I slumped against the wall, took a couple of deep breaths and persevered. Success! It was hidden amongst my underwear. I opened the window. Ray was standing patiently on the patio below.

'Coming!' I bellowed down at her and made my way tentatively downstairs.

Ray was spraying Wilf with the hose when I finally emerged. She looked up at me and grinned wildly when she saw me. 'Ready?!' she asked, eyes flashing with excitement.

'Yep,' I said, and removed my towel.

Ray burst out laughing.

'What?'

She couldn't answer, she'd completely lost it. I joined in. I couldn't help it; it was infectious.

'Oh Gus,' she said eventually, wiping tears from her face with the back of her hand, 'you look so cute and tiny!'

'So *ridiculous*,' I added.

Ray nodded.

'That too.'

Wilf bounded up to me nearly knocking me off my feet. But before I could scold him for it, I was hit by a barrage of ice-cold water. The shock of it stunned me into silence.

'Turn!' Ray instructed, so I did, several times.

'Enough?' Ray asked a few minutes later. My skin was covered in goose pimples.

'Yes,' I replied, shivering. Ray turned off the tap and handed me my towel. I wrapped it gratefully around me.

'I'll get you a smaller one for your head,' Ray said.

I was freezing, but it was worth it. I felt calm and cleansed, invigorated even. Ray reappeared at the doorway with another towel and motioned for me to come towards her.

'Come and sit with Mum by the fire.'

I willingly obliged.

'Better?' asked Mum.

'Much,' I nodded.

Mum reached out and rubbed my hand.

'Sorry,' I said quietly.

Mum furrowed her brow, confused.

'For getting drunk. For chucking up, and for being useless,' I lowered my eyes, embarrassed.

Mum cocked her head to one side.

'Don't be daft.'

I opened my mouth to protest, but Mum wouldn't let me.

'Sshhh,' she said softly, placing a finger to her lips. 'I get it.'

Her big brown eyes were warm and moist. I looked at her in awe. She'd done it again; she'd made me feel better.

'Come on,' she said patting me lightly on the back of my hand. 'Let's go into the lounge, Wimbledon's on in a bit.'

We all loved Wimbledon. It was a family favourite. The Oxford and Cambridge Boat Race was another; I watched it every year, without fail, even when I wasn't with Mum. We had no links or allegiance with either university but every year we picked a crew and passionately cheered them on. I knew it was something I would do forever.

My stomach growled.

'Hungry?' Mum asked.

'Starving!' I replied, rubbing my stomach. 'Do you think Dad's offer of eggs still stands?'

Mum smiled and winked at me.

'He'll make 'em if I tell him to.'

She was right. He would. Mum would insist, and right now none of us could refuse her a single thing.

CHAPTER 11

TIME

We travelled to the hospital in silence, each consumed by our own thoughts. We decided to go in one car to save on parking and I was grateful to be behind the wheel; driving was a good distraction. Today we would find out exactly how Mum had responded to cycle three. I glanced up at my rear-view mirror. She certainly looked well. She was wearing her cropped salt and pepper wig for the first time and a red baker boy hat. Somehow, unbelievably, she was still a little tanned and her lips were painted ruby red. You wouldn't think she was ill. Perhaps she wasn't? Maybe the consultant who spoke to her on Friday was wrong? Her negative and ill-timed assessment of Mum's condition certainly didn't tally with the more optimistic attitude of the consultants we'd met with throughout the week. Maybe she hadn't been fully briefed and updated.

'Gus?'

I could see Ray peering at me in my peripheral vision.

'You've missed the turn,' she said quietly, pointing at the missed hospital entrance behind us. Bollocks!

'There's a lane at the bottom of this road,' said Mum. 'You can turn around there.'

A few minutes later we were crammed into a little white room awaiting the arrival of Dr Clarke. The door opened and Laura burst through red faced and windswept.

'Have I missed anything?' she panted.

We all shook our heads.

'Good, good.'

She looked frantically around her.

'We need more chairs,' she said breathlessly and breezed out of the room.

'Found one!' she announced five seconds later and plonked the blue plastic chair on the floor next to me. Before she sat down, she gave us all a quick hug.

'Okay?' I asked.

Laura pulled out her scrappy ponytail, ran her fingers through her hair, shook it loose and gathered it all back up again.

'Yes,' she replied. 'Tired. Seb was up most of the night.'

Just as I was about to reply, there was a light rap on the door and Dr Clarke walked in clutching Mum's file. I took a long deep breath to steady my nerves.

'All here, I see,' Dr Clarke said with a slight laugh.

'Of course!' Laura shot back.

Dr Clarke sat himself down and placed Mum's file on the desk beside him. He looked directly at Mum.

'How are you, Sally?'

'Okay,' Mum nodded.

'You look well,' he smiled, sitting back in his chair and crossing his legs.

'Well,' he began, 'it's all looking rather good.'

Silence.

'Your bloods are still normal, and your bone marrow is faultless.'

I gripped onto the sides of my chair.

'Faultless?'

Dr Clarke turned his head towards Laura.

'Yes,' he replied. 'Faultless.'

Ray and I exchanged a baffled expression. Laura forced him to elaborate.

'So?' she pressed.

Dr Clarke folded his arms across his protruding stomach. 'So,' he continued, 'Cycle three has had an effect.'

'The leukaemia's gone?!' Ray blurted out. Dr Clarke held up one of his hands, silencing her.

'Not completely,' he said leaning forward slightly, 'it *looks* as though the leukaemia has gone, but in actual fact it's just hiding.'

He looked at us all one by one, before resting his gaze on Mum. 'Your leukaemia will return; we've seen hallmarks of the disease in your stem cells. It might not be for months, possibly years, but it *will* return.' He took Mum's hands in his own. 'You've achieved a partial remission. But knowing what we do about your stem cells, unfortunately, we can't press ahead with more treatment.'

I was utterly confused.

'Why not?' I asked. 'Surely another cycle of the same drugs

would *build* on this cycle's success and wipe out the leukaemia completely.'

Dr Clarke let go of Mum's hands and sat back in his chair, releasing a big sigh.

'I see where you're coming from,' he replied. 'But more chemo would be incredibly risky; it's not something we're prepared to do.'

Laura sat up tall in her chair.

'What about a transplant?'

Dr Clarke shook his head. 'Afraid not, and the reason for this is two-fold. First, your Mum would need more chemo and as I've already said this isn't something we're prepared to do. Secondly, she needs a match and neither of her brothers qualify.'

None of us knew what to say.

'Further treatment would seriously hamper the quality of life that you have left. Go and enjoy the extra time this cycle has given you. At the moment you are well, Sally, and you *could* be for a very long time. We can give you maintenance chemo to keep your leukaemia at bay, and,' he paused, 'you never know, the maintenance chemo could, and I stress *could*, rid you of the disease altogether. It's happened once before.'

My brain hurt. I was properly confused.

'But,' I said, somewhat pained, 'you just said more chemo was futile and would hamper her quality of life.'

Dr Clarke nodded.

'Strong cycles of chemo, yes. Maintenance chemo doesn't pose the same outright risks. It's the best option all round.'

'And it might even *destroy* the disease?' I leaned forward

slightly, digging my fingers deeper into the sides of my chair.

'Highly unlikely,' Dr Clarke replied, 'but, as I say, it's happened once before.'

'So,' said Ray, her voice small and tight, 'there's still hope?'

And that at the end of the day was all we really needed to know. It was a long while before Dr Clarke spoke.

'Yes,' he said, eventually, 'you still have hope.'

I closed my eyes. Relief flooded through me. Mum was going nowhere, not for a while anyway. We had time and quite possibly lots of it, and if we were *really* lucky, she'd be with us for years! I felt a surge of love and pride. Together we were a formidable force. All we had to do was stay strong and positive. I threw my head back and puffed out my cheeks. Cycle three had defied them all, and if anyone could beat the odds, Mum could. I'd never been more convinced of anything in my entire life.

Dr Clarke stood to leave.

'Maintenance chemo it is then.'

We all nodded, enthusiastically.

'You won't need it right away. We'll get you in every few weeks for monitoring and start the chemo as and when it's needed. My secretary will be in touch.'

'Great,' replied Mum. 'Thank you.'

'Go and celebrate,' he said warmly. 'It's a glorious day.'

It certainly was.

'You can do this, Mum,' I said, giving her a big squeeze.

Mum's eyes filled with tears.

'*We* can,' she corrected, squeezing my hand. '*We* can.'

We filed out of the room, tripping over each other with

excitement and almost knocked over a nurse and his trolley. It was Steve.

'Sorry,' I said sweetly, pushing my fringe out of my eyes. Steve smiled warmly.

'No worries,' he said.

He looked at Mum and squinted.

'Sally?'

Mum nodded.

'Hi Steve,' she said. 'How are you?'

'Very well thank you,' he said, taking her in. 'As are you by the look of things!'

'She's doing *really* well,' Ray replied proudly, on Mum's behalf. 'We're going home,' she continued, 'for good!'

Steve raised his eyebrows.

'Really?! That's fabulous!'

We all beamed at him.

'Well,' Steve began, 'take care and good luck!' He offered his hand for Mum to shake.

'Thank you,' she said.

'Cheerio,' Steve smiled as he turned to leave.

We waved him off and eagerly headed for the exit.

The seagull was dangerously close. It was tottering about on the roof of the building next to where we were sitting, eyeballing me. It wanted my scone. It inched closer. I flinched. Dad laughed.

'Just ignore it,' he said, taking a huge mouthful of his own scone.

'I can't,' I replied, 'it's staring at me!'

'I didn't realise seagulls were so big,' Ray remarked.

'Pesky freeloaders,' I muttered and shifted further away in my seat. 'Bugger off!'

Dad tore off a piece of his scone and threw it over the balcony railing and onto the ground below. I looked at him, agog. 'What the hell did you do that for?!'

Dad shrugged and smiled.

'It was bothering you,' he replied nonchalantly. 'Now it's gone.'

I rolled my eyes. 'You don't get rid of a seagull by giving it *food*. It'll come back now, expecting more and will probably peck all our eyes out!'

'Only yours, 'Dad said, his eyes twinkling.

'If it comes back, you can sit in my seat,' Mum offered. 'I'm half blind anyway.'

Me, Ray, Mum and Dad had driven to the harbour after our meeting with Dr Clarke. And after a gentle stroll in the blazing heat, we'd stopped for a cream tea. It was delicious.

'Why don't we have a BBQ this weekend?' Ray suggested. 'Get Laura and the boys down, celebrate properly?'

'Sounds like a good idea to me,' Dad said.

'I haven't seen the boys in so long ...' Mum said, spreading a thick layer of jam onto her scone.

Neither had I.

'Now that everything's a bit more stable,' she began, 'I'm

going to move back south, stay with your father at his flat and come back to Devon for monitoring.'

'Really?' Ray asked, a little taken aback.

Mum nodded.

'You've all given up your lives to be with me in Devon. It's time for you and Kate to go back home, get back to your men, your work. If I base myself at your Dad's, I'll be able to see you *all* and at your convenience.'

It certainly made a lot of sense, but the idea of leaving her terrified me. This bizarre yet incredible existence had been my world for almost eight weeks, I wasn't sure I *could* go back.

Mum narrowed her eyes at me.

'You don't think it's a good idea?' she asked.

I pulled down the sleeves of my cardigan past my fingers and lowered my eyes. 'Yes,' I replied. 'It's just, 'I don't like the idea of not seeing you every day, of not looking after you.'

Mum reached over and gently rubbed my arm.

'You need a break Kate-kins,' she said looking at Ray and then back at me as her eyes filled with tears. 'You both do. You've done so much for me and I'm more grateful than you'll ever know but,' she sat back in her chair, put down the knife she was holding and linked arms with Dad, 'you need to return home; get back to the men who love you.'

I did. *We* did. I missed Chris terribly, but it wasn't something I allowed myself to think about. Devon was where I was needed and where I wanted to be; missing Chris didn't really come into it. Ray reached out and hugged me. We eventually pulled apart and looked at each other.

'What will I do without my Gus, Gus?'

A lump lodged itself in my throat. I didn't, couldn't reply.

'Tweedledee and Tweedledum,' Dad said affectionately, 'isn't that right love?'

Mum nodded and smiled at us both with pride.

My mobile started ringing. I looked at the screen: Chris.

'Hey,' I said, gathering myself together, 'we were just talking about you.'

'Yeah?' replied Chris, nervously.

'Don't worry, nothing bad.'

I switched ears to block out the noise of the table next to me. 'I've got some news actually.'

'Me too,' said Chris, 'but you first.'

'Mum's latest round of chemo appears to have done the trick!' I said with glee. 'It's not gone completely but she's out of the woods for the time being and has achieved a partial remission!'

It was the first time I'd said it out loud and it sounded wonderful.

'That's fantastic!' Chris replied, 'what – '

'And I'm coming home!' I squealed.

I could tell Chis was smiling.

'Brilliant!' he said, 'When?'

'Not sure,' I admitted. 'But soon. Probably after the weekend.'

'Cool, I guess I'd better tidy up,' he said with a chuckle.

'How bad is it?'

'Um …'

'Oh God!'

Chris sniggered.

'So, what's *your* news?' I asked.

'I've got a job interview.'

'Yay!' I replied. 'Where? When?'

'Rolls-Royce, next week.'

'That's amazing news!' I trilled. 'You've *always* wanted to work there!'

I sat back in my chair. Everything was starting to come together.

'If I get it,' Chris warned, 'we'd have to move to Derby.'

Maybe not.

'Derby?' I said slowly.

'Derby,' Chris repeated.

Mum was looking at me with a curious expression. Now wasn't the time to be negative.

'Well,' I began, 'we'll cross that bridge when we come to it,' I said and quickly changed the subject. 'Is it sunny where you are? It's lovely here.'

'Yep,' Chris sounded a little subdued.

Bum, I thought I'd gotten away with it.

'I'm sorry,' I pleaded, 'it's – '

'No, no,' Chris interjected, 'I'm not upset.' He paused and took a big breath. 'I've got something else to tell you.'

Whatever it was, I clearly wasn't going to like it.

'Anna's pregnant.'

I was right. I closed my eyes and said nothing.

'Kate?'

I felt sick.

'I'm here,' I said softly, swallowing hard.

'It's good news Kate; you're going to be an aunty again.'

I nodded. I didn't trust myself to speak. I loved Chris' sister and was genuinely thrilled for her, but every new pregnancy announcement – and they were never ending – hit me like a truck.

'How far along is she?' I croaked.

'Eight weeks.'

Chris' sister, Anna, was two years younger than me and had been married just six months. We had been married for over two years. I closed my eyes, tears rolling down my cheeks. It wasn't fair.

'It'll happen, babe,' Chris said softly.

Would it? We'd been trying for well over a year; it should've happened by now.

'When you get back,' Chris continued light-heartedly, 'we'll get properly stuck in and we'll make ourselves a big, fat baby.'

I giggled. Chris could always find a way to break through and make me laugh. But I wasn't ready to feel okay about this, my stomach was churning, and I knew I needed to cry and get it out of my system. So, I told him I loved him and quickly hung up. I dropped my head into my hands and sobbed my heart out.

'Oh sweetheart,' Mum soothed, stroking my head. 'What's wrong?'

It was a while before I could answer.

'Anna's pregnant,' I sniffed, wiping snot from my nose with my sleeve. 'Eight weeks.'

Dad looked bemused. He didn't know anything about my failed attempt to have kids. He got all his information about us from Mum and up until four weeks ago they'd been estranged.

'Chris and I have been trying for ages to get pregnant,' I explained, 'but it's not happening.' I sat up in my chair and sighed. 'Anna's pregnancy is just the latest in a long line of announcements, and it's getting harder and harder to take.'

I looked down at my hands, disheartened, and started picking at my nails.

'Doesn't mean to say it won't happen,' said Dad, matter-of-factly. 'For some couples it just takes a while.'

Mum nodded.

'Your Dad and I weren't always careful in the early days and I never fell pregnant accidently.' Mum stopped and smiled apologetically, 'All my drama probably hasn't helped.'

I looked up at her and furrowed my brow.

'Stress can play havoc with your hormones,' she said, jabbing Dad playfully in the ribs. 'Probably why I got breast cancer.'

'Might have known it'd be *my* fault.'

'Usually is,' said Ray, smiling.

Dad stuck his tongue out at Ray, gave Mum a quick kiss on the forehead and signalled to a waiter for the bill. I looked at the faces of my family, taking them in, one by one. It'd been a crazy few months. In a couple of days, it'd all be over and I'd no longer be with them. Mum's doctors had written her off *twice* in the last eight weeks. Yet here she was, dining al fresco in the hot summer sun like nothing had happened. I shook my head in disbelief.

'Your friend's back,' Dad said, pointing over my shoulder.

I followed his finger and came face to face with a big, fat

seagull. I turned to flee but tripped and fell. Mum, Dad and Ray collapsed into a fit of helpless laughter and teased me the entire way home.

CHAPTER 12

HOME

It hadn't taken long to pack and leave Devon, I simply gathered up all my clothes, knowing they'd all be thrown into the washing machine on my return, and stuffed them into my suitcase. I couldn't wait to wear something different, to have a proper shower and eat Chris' food. I often imagined our children ribbing me for my ghastly meals and begging for their Dad to come home early from work and take over. It was a fantasy I played out less and less these days. I looked up at the motorway sign above me – one more junction and I'd be on the M5; a third of the journey down, two thirds of the journey left to go.

I cast my mind back to last Saturday, the weekend of our BBQ. Everyone was there, Chris, Christian, Laura, Mark and the boys. It was bliss. The boys jumped around like loons in their pants all day. Me, Laura and Ray prepared and cooked the food and Dad, as usual, took charge of the boiler and the log burner. It was idyllic; like something out of *The Waltons*. But in the evening, something sad and unexpected happened. At about eleven there was a loud crash from the downstairs toilet.

Ray immediately went to investigate. A couple of minutes later she appeared at the lounge doorway and motioned for me to join her.

'What is it?' I whispered.

'It's Darcy,' said Ray, her eyes wide with panic.

I looked at her with a puzzled expression and dutifully followed her. Ray opened the door. Darcy was lying on her side, completely still. I took a step back. It didn't look like she was breathing. Ray knelt down beside her.

'I think she's dead,' she said, caressing Darcy's head.

I dropped to my knees placing one hand on Darcy's ribs, the other in front of her mouth. Nothing. Shit. How was this possible? She'd been running around with Wilf all day; it was the most animated I'd seen her in weeks!

'Mum will be devastated.'

'I know,' I agreed.

We got up and walked slowly back to the lounge.

'Mum?' Ray said, gently.

It was obvious something was wrong. Ray and I were hopeless at masking our emotions.

'What's happened?' Mum demanded.

'Darcy …' she replied, slowly lifting her eyes to meet Mum's.

Mum barged her way past us and into the hall with Dad in pursuit and Ray and I lagging behind. On seeing Darcy, Mum fell to the floor, hands covering her mouth. Dad remained standing; his arms crossed firmly across his chest as Mum lowered herself towards Darcy's ear and started whispering.

'My beautiful girl, my beautiful girl, thank you, thank you!'

I looked away; it was too much. Making my way back to the lounge, I filled in the others. It was a while before Mum returned. She stayed in that little room saying her goodbyes for almost half an hour. The rest of us just waited. When she was done Dad wrapped Darcy in a big, warm blanket, at Mum's request, and carried her carefully to the shed outside.

I went to bed that night feeling strangely at peace. The timing of Darcy's death felt like a sign; a green light to leave; the end of an era.

The next morning Ray came quietly giggling into my room and told me that Christian feared he might have had something to do with it. He'd apparently had an almighty shit just moments before and had convinced himself that the potent stench he'd created had shocked the life out of her! It was the funniest thing I'd heard in ages and kept me chuckling for the rest of the day.

I glanced at my dashboard; I needed petrol. I'd clocked it earlier and made a mental note to stop at the services before the M5 turn-off. Walking back to my car after I'd paid for my fuel, I noticed a familiar small, black car. It looked like Ray's car. I squinted. It *was* Ray's car. Ray grinned sheepishly and waved. I marched over as she rolled down her window.

'I didn't know you were still behind me,' I said, surprised.

She looked up at me, her eyes moist.

'I couldn't leave you.'

My heart swelled. She pushed open her car door and threw her arms around me, almost choking me.

'When will I next see you?' she asked, her voice small and sad.

'Soon,' I assured her.

'It had better be,' Ray warned and released herself from our embrace.

'There'll be loads of opportunities,' I promised, 'and we'll speak all the time.'

Ray nodded and wiped away a tear.

'Silly ol' goon!' I teased.

Ray pulled a face, wounded.

Laughing, I ruffled the top of her head before pulling her in for another embrace. 'Now get back in the car,' I ordered, once we'd parted, 'and go home!'

'Okay,' she replied, reluctantly.

I thought about Ray and how close we'd become all the way home. We'd always been close, and had always had fun together, but being with each other, day in, day out for such an intense amount of time, had taken us somewhere new. There was a trust and a mutual respect that hadn't always been there before.

Perhaps most significantly, Ray had taught me to slow down, to take my time. What was the rush? She'd say, we weren't in a race; no need to panic; it would all still get done. I lived my life at breakneck speed and for the first time ever I was walking instead of running and it suited me. I tried to push her around in the beginning, assigning roles and so on, but Ray's laissez-faire attitude quickly and unexpectedly rubbed off on me. And just like she said they would, things got done.

The only problem I had with this more 'relaxed' approach was that it sometimes made us late, and I *hate* being late, anywhere. Punctuality is important to me. It shows people I care. We all get caught out from time to time – roadworks, delayed services, an early morning mishap – but more often than not the reason for tardiness is simple and inexcusable: poor planning. Well, that's how I used to see it. But really, what *was* so bad about being a few minutes late? Sometimes it mattered – interviews, meetings, weddings – sometimes it didn't. If the person you've arranged to meet for coffee is late – have another coffee and enjoy the alone time. Likewise, if your dinner date's running behind schedule, order a glass of wine and soak up the ambience. Getting wound up about it, I'd come to realise, was futile. Life is full of enough stress and drama, why create more?

Mum didn't scold me or think less of me when we showed up a little later than expected at hospital. In fact, she didn't even seem to notice, she was just glad we were there at all. I'd always feared that if I turned up somewhere late, I'd be branded lazy, thoughtless, arrogant. This would be unfair and inaccurate. I was too much of a perfectionist to allow for the possibility of it. But the only person judging me, was me.

I'd also learnt to let go a bit. I like to lead, to take the initiative. However, in my desire to get things moving I didn't always think things through and often I'd find myself wishing I'd taken a bit more time, sat with it a bit more. Ray approached tasks differently. She *saw* things differently. Less concerned with speed and completion, she focussed on the here and now, the A to B not the A to Z. It made a helluva lot of sense. In fact, a lot of what Ray said and did made a helluva lot of sense. Up until a few weeks ago she'd just been my adorable, happy-go-lucky baby sis, forever fourteen. Not anymore. Ray had looked up to me her entire life. For the *rest* of it, we'd be eye to eye.

I was struggling to concentrate. My boss wanted a financial breakdown of the past month's fundraising activity in Buckinghamshire, but I kept drifting off. My heart simply wasn't in it. I'd been fully briefed on all that had gone on in my patch while I'd been away and was now expected to pick up where I'd left off. Somehow though I just couldn't quite muster up the enthusiasm and motivation required. There was so much to do; it all felt a little overwhelming.

I didn't want to be here. I no longer felt as though I belonged. The phone rang incessantly, the emails were endless, so many demands, so much noise. Was this how it had always been? I longed for the peace of Devon and the company of my family. I didn't want to have to spend my days justifying low-income streams to my bosses; you couldn't *force* people to fundraise. But try telling that to the big bods. Fundraising is a surprisingly ruthless business. Like most charities, Macmillan relies on the generosity of the public to fund its services which means people like me – Fundraising Managers – have to ensure a certain amount of money keeps coming in each and every month to pay for them. People and businesses pulled out of projects and events all the time. It was common for companies to 'over promise' and then fail to deliver. As partnerships rolled on, company initiatives inevitably took over, relegating any agreed upon fundraising efforts, to the bottom of the priority pile. It was hard to control and very, *very* frustrating.

I used to thrive on the challenge of it all, but not anymore. It's tough out there, for me, for everyone, and I no longer wanted to chase people or motivate them to continue fundraising – it was *their* life, *their* choice, and if a decision had been taken to stop, who the hell was I to try to convince them otherwise? No matter what, we *always* have a choice. I looked at my computer screen and smiled. I don't have to do this. I don't have to *sit* here and do this! I'd already reduced my hours to four days a week so that I could travel on a Friday to be with Mum, so why not just quit completely? Do something else? I'd done it before. Life was short and unexpected; I had to fill my days with passion and purpose. I glanced up at the clock on the wall: 3.30 pm. It was doable. Focus and it was definitely doable.

I'd taken pregnancy tests countless times before, so peeing on a stick was nothing new. The only difference this time was that instead of waiting and hoping for a blue line to appear, I was waiting for a smiley face. The face would confirm that I was ovulating. I didn't really need to take the test – I'd been monitoring and obsessing over my menstrual cycle for almost a year and a half, and I hadn't noticed anything unusual. I was regular and experienced all the expected symptoms and changes. Checking wouldn't hurt though, especially as we'd been trying for so long. I looked down at the stick: I was ovulating. I slumped against the back of the toilet, relieved. It didn't last long. If I was ovulating and menstruating normally, then why hadn't it happened yet? I stood up, threw the test in the bin and stomped out of the bathroom. Chris would be back any minute. I planned to pounce on him as soon as he walked through the front door. A sex marathon was in order; I was ovulating. I sat myself on our bed and waited.

'You're fucking unbelievable!'

Chris was sitting half up in bed, his shirt off and trousers fastened. I was standing up, glowering at him, incensed.

'How can you just,' I made quotation marks in the air with my hands, 'not be up for it?!'

He didn't respond.

'Men are always up for it!' I spat. 'Why not you?'

Chris dragged his eyes from the floor to my face.

'I'm tired.'

'You're *tired*?!' I replied. I crossed my arms. 'Well *I'm* ovulating and in case you'd forgotten, we're trying to make a baby!'

Chris continued to stare at me.

'I know we are,' he said softly. 'We had sex last night and this morning – '

'Too much sex is a problem for you?!' I interrupted, eyes blazing.

He sighed and looked up at the ceiling.

'Well?' I pushed. 'Is it?!'

I watched as he closed his eyes, blocking me out. But I was on a roll.

'Men don't turn down sex!' I bent over and nudged him on the arm, provoking him, 'What's wrong with you?!'

'I don't have to listen to this,' he said, getting up off the bed and heading towards the door.

I went after him, grabbing his arm and stopping him.

'Oh yes you do!' I replied. 'This is important!'

'You're being unreasonable.'

I released my grip on his arm.

'I'm being unreasonable?'

'Yes!' Chris shot back.

I could feel tears pooling in my eyes. I willed them away.

'What's so unreasonable about wanting a baby with the man I love?'

Chris' face softened slightly.

'Nothing.'

I dropped onto the bed and let the tears flow. Chris sat down beside me and covered my hands with his, rubbing the tip of my thumb. I didn't like the way I was behaving. I was being irrational, desperate, hysterical. It was all really starting to get to me. I needed to breathe, calm down. I walked over to my discarded clothes, yanked them back on and unhooked my jacket from the inside of the wardrobe door.

'I'm going for a walk,' I sniffed.

Chris' forehead creased with worry.

'I'll be fine,' I reassured him and kissed the top of his head. 'I need some air.'

I found my shoes, grabbed my keys, and headed for the door.

I shouldn't have left the flat. The park was heaving with happy families enjoying the last of the day's sun. So much for escapism. The life I yearned for and could quite possibly be denied was being rammed down my goddamned throat. Blissed out mums chatted and strolled with their pregnant chums while dressed down dads kicked balls about with their tottering sons. It was an idyllic nightmare. A little girl, aged about three or four, pedalled past me, her face determined. She rang the bell on her handlebars and looked back searching for her dad. He was a few metres back and staring at her with idiotic pride. 'Whoo-hoo!' he cried, 'That's my girl! You've got it!"

The little girl grinned back at him, delighting in his praise and attention.

'Keep going,' the man enthused. 'Daddy's right behind you.'

I closed my eyes and took a long, deep breath. I'd bought a book on meditation a few days back and had read through some of the exercises during my lunch breaks at work. The last few months had taken their toll; I was mentally and physically exhausted. I hoped meditation might help to restore some balance back to my body and get me in a healthy state of mind. I'd been inspired to try it after watching Mum's response to the reiki treatment she'd had at the hospital shortly after her last chemo. I was sceptical at first – reiki was an ancient spiritual healing practice developed by Buddhists in Japan. It was all about restoring equilibrium to the body and the energy flow between patient and practitioner. Dad didn't hold back, 'a load of mumbo jumbo,' he'd scoffed, but the rest of us were intrigued and encouraged Mum to try it. The difference in her after the treatment was nothing short of astonishing. She glowed. She told us she felt 'cleansed,' and during the treatment had seen little men inside her body working tirelessly together destroying all the leukemic cells. Two weeks later we'd found out the cycle had been a partial success. Had the reiki had anything to do with it? It was impossible to say, but Mum certainly felt better afterwards.

I took another deep breath and began one of the visualisation techniques in the book. I had to focus on what I wanted and visualise it happening. I pictured myself holding my baby and held onto the image for ten deep breaths. After I'd completed the exercise, I tried something else. Before we left Devon, Ray and I had a long chat about guardian angels in Mum's garden. Ray very much believed in them. 'Talk to them,' she encouraged. 'Invite them in; ask them to help.' It sounded a little wacky but hell, nothing really made much sense anymore. I looked nervously around me, then quietly began to explain what had happened, the difficulty Chris and I were having in getting pregnant and asked the angels to help us. I wanted proof that I'd been heard so I finished up by saying I'd reopen my eyes in ten seconds and look around for a sign. I counted to ten in my head and tentatively opened my eyes.

I scanned the ground below me. Nothing. I turned my head

to my left and looked down. My stomach did a little flip. A little white feather was resting on the arm of the bench I was sitting on. I picked it up and inspected it. It was pristine and as white as freshly laid snow. It freaked me out a little. Had the feather been there all along? If it had, I would have noticed, surely? I shook my head, bemused, and carefully tucked the feather into my jacket pocket.

CHAPTER 13

EBB AND FLOW

Mum sounded terrible, 'I'm okay,' she spluttered. 'It's just a cold.'

We had been on the phone for about five minutes, and she'd spent the majority of the call coughing.

'Have you been to the doctors?' I asked.

'No need,' she replied, her voice small and strained. 'I feel better than I did yesterday, and the sun will help.'

Mum and Dad were going to Sicily for a few weeks; they were off later that evening. They'd talked about a longer trip to Australia but because of her condition Mum was only allowed to travel within Europe. I didn't like the idea of her being out of the country, but we all agreed the trip was a good idea.

'I hope it doesn't ruin your holiday,' I said.

'Me too,' Mum agreed before exploding into another coughing fit. It made me wince.

'Sorry,' she whispered, almost a minute later.

'Don't apologise,' I replied. 'Just keep taking the drugs and drink lots of water.'

'Did you bother with the ovulation test sticks in the end?'

She said, changing the subject.

'Yep,' I replied, running my hand through my hair wearily.

'And how are you feeling?'

'Bored, frustrated,' I admitted.

'At least you know you're okay,' Mum said brightly.

'S'pose.'

'It'll happen, darling,' Mum said after a moment. 'Just hang on in there.'

It had been a week since I'd ovulated, and as usual, I was obsessing, looking for signs, looking up symptoms. I tried not to, but it was impossible; the web made it way too easy.

'My breasts feel quite sore,' I admitted.

Mum sneezed.

'I had a really bad headache yesterday too,'

I knew I sounded ridiculous.

'When's your period due?' Mum asked.

'Five days. Well,' I elaborated, 'five days if it's on time, which it usually is.'

There was a loud smash in the background.

'Oh for fuck's sake!'

It was Dad.

'I'd better go and see what your father's up to,' Mum said.

'Good idea. It doesn't sound good.'

'Try not to obsess about it all,' she smiled.

'I'll try. But only if *you* promise not to overdo it out there.'

'I promise.'

'Good,' I said. 'Look after yourself and text me when you arrive.'

'Will do,' Mum promised.

'Love you.'

'Love you, too.'

I handed in my notice. Four more weeks and I'd be free! My boss said she wasn't surprised; she could see I was struggling and fully understood. I had no immediate plans to start looking for something else; I'd think about that later. Right now, I just needed some space. I didn't like being away from Mum. I wanted to keep a closer eye on her; being apart from her just felt wrong. I tried to get back into the swing of my old life, but I was failing miserably. Chris and I had gone out a few times with friends, and although it was enjoyable, a big part of me struggled. I couldn't relate to them or their trivial concerns. I felt trapped and alone. I was frightened too. What if I'd always feel this way?

I sat slumped on the loo and sobbed. So much for sodding angels! I peered at the bloody water below, balled my fists, punched the cabinet next to me and screamed. I lost it, completely and utterly. On the bathroom floor beside me – a ripped up a box of Tampax and a dozen or so unopened tampons. Why wasn't it happening?! I slammed the back of my head into the wall behind me. Hot fat tears spilled from my eyes. Something had to be wrong.

I headed to the kitchen. Grabbing a handful of carrots from the fridge, I started chopping. I needed to focus on something, anything.

'Kate?'

Chris was home. I didn't answer. I didn't trust myself to speak.

'Kate?' he called again, a little louder.

I continued chopping, fast and carelessly.

'Here you are! Why didn't you answer?'

He reached for a glass above my head, kissed me on the cheek and turned towards the sink. I dare not look at him. The news I so desperately wanted to give him, I couldn't.

'Easy!' Chris laughed, filling the glass with water. 'You'll cut yourself.'

I continued to chop.

'Everything okay?' he asked.

I closed my eyes and dropped the knife, silent tears streaming down my face. Chris pulled me in for an embrace, but I pushed him away.

'What on earth's the matter?'

I'd have to tell him. I couldn't put it off any longer. I rarely, if ever, refused a hug. I leant back and gripped the top of the work surface for support. I opened my eyes and looked straight into his.

'I got my period.'

I said it quietly and without emotion. Chris lowered his eyes and then his head. A lump the size of a golf ball was wedged in my throat. I tried to speak, 'I – '

Chris shook his head and gathered me up tightly into his arms.

'Enough,' he said, purposefully.

Enough? I released myself from his grip and looked up at him, confused. He placed his hands either side of my face.

'Time to get tested.'

Fresh tears filled my eyes.

'I'll call the docs first thing Monday morning.'

I threw my arms around his waist and burrowed my face deep into his chest.

Italy was a disaster. Mum was ill the entire time. The air conditioning hadn't helped. They managed a little sightseeing towards the end when Mum felt a bit better, but mostly they were confined to loungers by the pool. Mum insisted it hadn't been a wasted trip; she'd enjoyed the heat at least. She certainly sounded better than she had before she left, which was a relief.

I glanced at my mobile for the umpteenth time. Mum was back in Devon today for monitoring. Ray had accompanied her and promised to call with an update. The call came an hour later.

'Ray?'

Silence. A chill ripped through me.

'Ray? I tried again.

'It's back, Gus,' Ray whimpered, 'the leukaemia's back.'

Already? My stomach lurched into my throat.

'Gus?'

'I'm here,' I croaked.

'She's properly pissed,' Ray said with a sad little laugh.

'I'm not surprised!' I replied.

'Effing and blinding all over the place; you'd be proud.'

'And you?' I asked, gently. 'How are you?'

'Same as you I suspect. Shocked, angry, numb.'

'And where's Mum now?'

'Talking to one of the nurses.'

'What about?'

'Maintenance chemo.'

'How high is her white blood count?'

'Not too bad, but without chemo it'll slowly start to creep up.'

I removed my glasses and rubbed my eyes, smudging my mascara. It was all happening way too soon. Months, they'd said – possibly a year.

'Do they think it'll work?' I asked, flatly.

'They didn't really say.'

'And how often will she have to have it?'

'Every week.'

I puffed out my cheeks, closed my eyes and sat back in my chair. This time last year Mum was happy and cancer free. She'd fought and won. Isolated for so long, we decided to throw her a big birthday party. Mum loved parties. She hosted several at our family home including a spectacular Halloween bash to celebrate turning forty, and a Hollywood themed shindig for her fiftieth. Mum and Dad had dressed up as Fred and Wilma Flintstone. Dad's transformation was a little unnerving – I'd never seen him with a full head of hair. The parties were big, loud and lots of fun. This party would be a quieter affair, but it'd give us all a chance to let our hair down and most importantly allow Mum to feel alive again. Sadness washed over me. What if that party was to be her last?

'She could still achieve remission,' Ray said quietly.

I smiled, admiring her resolve.

'I know,' I replied.

'Oh,' Ray began. 'Mum wants to know if Chris has got his results back?'

I shook my head in disbelief. She'd just been told her leukaemia was back, but her thoughts were with me.

'No, not yet,' I replied. 'Now, get back to Mum and I'll call Laura.'

'Okay.'

'And give Mum a hug from me.'

'Will do.'

Two days later Mum was back at Dad's flat and feeling good, convinced she was on the right drug. We had no option but to go along with it; what we truly believed was irrelevant. What we were *definitely* in agreement about though was a second opinion. We did some research and got in touch with a leukaemia specialist at The Royal Marsden – a cancer hospital in Surrey. Ray emailed him, outlined Mum's case and asked for an assessment. We had no idea if we'd get a response, but we had to try. Mum wasn't giving up, so neither were we.

CHAPTER 14

BOMBSHELL 2

I drummed my fingers nervously on my work desk. Fifteen more minutes and I'd be free to go. Chris was getting the results of his sperm test today and I'd spent the entire day glancing at my mobile willing it to ring. But it hadn't and the day was drawing to a close. What did this mean? Chris and I hadn't agreed to speak to each other, but I assumed he'd call and update me. Perhaps he hadn't called because his results were still at the lab. He wouldn't keep me hanging if the news was bad, would he? Ten minutes to go.

I decided to make a call to a volunteer. I chose Val – a big-hearted bubbly grandmother who could chat for hours. The minutes would zip by. I looked up her number and waited for the line to connect. Val was still going twenty minutes later. Damn it! I tried to wind up the call but Val was on a roll. Her devoted pooch had an ear infection. He was miserable and off his food. What did I suggest? Five minutes later I'd had enough and cut her off with a little white lie. My boss was on the other line. It was urgent. I had to go. I glanced at the clock. It was twenty minutes past five. I gathered up my bits, turned off my computer and ran to my car.

I drove into our flat's communal parking area and spotted Chris' car straight away. He was home. He could have called. Why hadn't he called? I parked in the space next to Chris and switched off the engine. Taking a couple of deep breaths, I opened the car door. Everything was about to change. Problem or no problem, I'd have my answer. Stepping gingerly out of the car, I rolled my shoulders and fixed my gaze on our flat, willing myself on. I told myself I'd look back at this moment and laugh. I was sure of it. Climbing the communal stairs, I stopped outside our front door. I needed a few more seconds. I reached for the handle, hesitated and put my ear to the door. Silence. I was being ridiculous. Standing up, I smoothed down my fringe and gently pushed the door.

'Hey?' I said, nervously.

No answer. I continued past the spare room coming to an abrupt stop just outside our bedroom. Chris was in the lounge, rocking from one foot to the other, his hand rubbing his chin. He was still wearing his coat. He stole a quick glance at me, but he couldn't hold my gaze. His eyes darted to the floor. Shit.

'It isn't good,' he stammered.

I dropped my handbag.

'There's a problem,' he said, unable to look at me.

I'd stopped breathing.

'They couldn't find any sperm in my sample.'

The room tilted. No sperm. No sperm *at all*. Was this even possible? Sperm could be faulty or low in number, but all men produced it. Didn't they?

'Kate?'

I turned towards the window, unable to look at him.

'Kate?'

I could see Chris staring at me from the corner of my eye. I started to sway. I wasn't going to be a mother. I clamped a hand over my mouth. This wasn't happening. A surge of heat rushed through me.

No sperm.

My legs buckled. Not a single one. I reached for the arm of the sofa and slowly lowered myself into it. My other hand was still clamped to my mouth. I was trembling. Tears filled my eyes. I looked up at Chris. His pale face was staring straight back at me, blue eyes moist and full of pain. My hand slipped from my mouth and rested on my chest. There was no going back. The moment I had lived in fear of was here and there was nothing I could do about it.

No sperm.

It was as bad as it could possibly be. I shook my head in disbelief. Chris – hands balled into fists by his side – gave a quick nod of his head and closed his eyes. A single tear rolled down his cheek. That was it. I couldn't keep it together a second longer.

'Oh God!' I wailed, over and over.

I pulled my legs up to my chest and buried my face between my knees.

No sperm.

No children.

No future.

Mum, I needed Mum. I jumped up off the sofa, dived into my handbag, retrieved my mobile and ran outside. Collapsing onto a patch of grass by the side of our building, I found Mum's number and hit call. She answered after just one ring. I tried to speak, to explain, but I couldn't find the words. Mum listened patiently to me sob, gently reminding me to 'breathe' and to 'take my time.'

'I'm never going to be Mum,' I said eventually.

Silence.

'Chris has no sperm.'

I heard Mum take a sharp intake of breath.

'None at all,' I said.

I wiped my nose on the cuff of my top and sniffed.

'So that's that. We're buggered. Well and truly. Just as well Laura's had three.'

It was a while before Mum spoke.

'How's Chris?' she asked.

'Dunno.'

'You don't know?!'

'He told me, I lost it and ran outside and called you.'

Mum sighed.

'Kate, he must feel terrible. You have to talk to him. You're in this together. He needs you.'

Shame washed over me.

'Go back inside,' Mum insisted. 'Call me later.'

I plucked a blade of grass from the ground, pushed myself up onto my feet and walked back into the flat. Chris was leaning against the wall in the lounge, head bowed. He looked so scared, so hurt. He didn't turn to look at me. What to say? I wanted to let him know how much I loved him, to reassure him that this was our problem, not his. It wasn't his fault. I desperately tried to organise my thoughts and say what I needed to, but Chris beat me to it.

'You should leave me.'

What? Where the hell did that come from?!

'I can't give you want you want,' he said. 'What you deserve. If you stay with me, I'll make you unhappy and I don't want that … all I've ever wanted is for you to be happy.'

I stared at him, disbelieving. Chris didn't say things by accident or speak for the sake of it. He meant this. He wasn't looking for sympathy. This is what he believed. What he'd been turning over in his mind while I'd been outside. I was about to tell him to stop being so ridiculous but was silenced once more by a noise I had only recently heard for the very first time in Devon; a wail, like Mum's, from deep within.

Chris doubled over and burst into tears. I was horrified. I had never seen my husband cry before. I fought back a smile. It was a smile born out of fear. Fear of the unknown. This was new territory. I hadn't been here before. The strong, dependable man I loved had been beaten and the tears had found a way through. I looked on in stunned silence, completely torn. I desperately wanted to reach out and hug him, but my gut told me to leave him, let him be. He needed to do this; to cry it all out. For me crying had always been a release. It was a good thing; it enabled me to get to the other side, to move forward. Leave him? No way! The very idea! But I could see how he had reached this conclusion. He knew how badly I wanted kids. He took on my pain. He always had. And I let him. It lightened my load. I leaned on him way too much. If I was upset, so was he. If I was happy, so was he. His desire for my happiness above all else was ridiculous. He would do absolutely anything for me. It was evident almost from the start. He'd told me over dinner one night at university that if I ever cheated on him or fell out of love with him, he wouldn't fight for me. You'd just let me go? I challenged, hurt and confused – the woman you loved? Yes, I'd want you to be happy, he explained. And if that meant a life without me then so be it. It took me a while to get my head around what he was saying to me, but eventually I understood. With Chris I was free. He allowed me to be me. Caught up, like so many hormonal teens in the passion-crazed love affair of Romeo and Juliet, it took me a while to fully appreciate this low budget, no frills alternative. With Chris I was safe. Juliet – bewitched and destroyed by the obsessive actions of a selfish young man – was not. Chris would never force my hand or make life difficult for me. The only time he ever got cross was when someone upset me. He hated seeing me in pain. How ironic then that the biggest pain I'd ever known should be caused, unintentionally, by him.

'This is all my fault ...' he said. 'We can't have a baby because of me ... I'm useless ... I'm pointless ... I'm a genetic dead end ... I can't give you want you want ... I've let you down ...I've ruined our future ... leave me, please, you're better off without me ...'

I tell him I love him, over and over. It's all I can say. Eventually, he calmed down, sat down on the sofa next to me, grabbed my hands and gently rested his forehead against mine.

We sat on the sofa, silent and entwined for the rest of the evening. There was nothing we could do or say that would make us feel any better, so we stayed where we were. Mum text me offering her support, as did Laura and Ray. Laura told me to ring and rant if I needed to, which was sweet, but the thought of it left me cold. Laura had what I wanted. She'd conceived with ease. Ours was a situation she knew nothing about, talking to her about it would do me no good at all. I was angry, upset and confused. We'd been dealt the cruellest of blows and were somehow going to have to find a way to live with it.

We tried and failed to sleep. The doctor who called Chris with the results advised him to provide another sample, just in case. Sperm is very sensitive, apparently. The sample might have been left out too long, killing off all the sperm. Sounded unlikely, the test result matched our lack of success, and surely the sperm would still be visible? At some ungodly hour Chris rolled over, draped his arm across my waist, pressed up tightly against me and drifted off.

I awoke to the sounds of chirping birds. Chris rubbed his eyes, checked the time on his phone and quickly sat up. He looked terrible.

'I've gotta get ready for work,' he said, reluctantly.

I reached out and pulled him tightly to me. I didn't want him to go. Chris let out a gentle laugh.

'You're choking me!'

'Sorry,' I giggled, and reluctantly let him go.

Chris leaned back and smiled.

'I love you.'

Tears pricked the back of my eyes.

'I love you too.'

It was ten o'clock. Mum, Ray and Laura were all on their way over to see me. I took some convincing that it was a good idea – the thought of being alone all day eventually swung it. They wouldn't stay long and promised to be gone by the time Chris got home from work. Mum was first through the door.

'We've bought cake!' she announced with a smile and marched quickly past me towards the kitchen.

Ray was standing right behind her and pulled me in for a big hug. It was all a bit too much. I pushed her away and apologised. She kissed me on the cheek and followed Mum to the kitchen. Laura was still in the car park. Mum and Ray had brought a load of savoury snacks as well. The plan, I was told, was to eat in the communal grounds outside.

A few minutes later while retrieving some juice from the fridge I heard a little giggle. I closed the door and came eye to eye with Nathaniel, Laura's three-year-old son. He was looking up at me mischievously; his bright blue eyes partly obscured by a gorgeous mop of unruly blonde curls. I bent down and scooped him up, squeezing him lovingly. He shook his head and wriggled free. He stared at the fridge door and pointed at a picture of Chris in a Santa hat.

'Chris is silly, isn't he?'

'He certainly is,' I replied.

'Hey,' Laura said, breathlessly, transferring her youngest from one hip to the other,

'beautiful day!'

I hadn't really noticed.

'That's why we're eating outside,' said Ray, face all aglow.

'Good idea,' said Laura.

She smiled at me warmly, stepped towards me and planted a kiss on my cheek.

'All done,' Mum announced, and handed me a plate of salmon.

It smelt divine. I hadn't eaten since lunchtime the day before. Nathaniel's eyes grew big and round.

'Hungry?' I asked, letting out a little laugh.

Nathaniel nodded. I grabbed his warm, plump little hand, and led him outside …

The day went well, their visit was a good distraction. And it was good to see Mum too. She looked so well and, as usual, I found myself staring at her in awe. Her future was even more uncertain than mine, but it was my life not hers that concerned her. She told me over and over not to give up; our situation, she insisted, was far from hopeless. I wished more than anything that she didn't have to come here and console me. She'd been through enough crap over the last few years. Causing her additional pain and worry, upset me enormously.

Chris and I parked outside the doctors' surgery. The second sample had once again shown an absence of any sperm. Chris did everything he could to make sure he handed it in quickly – wanking in the hospital toilet and giving his sample to the nurse on reception just seconds later. I couldn't help but laugh – all those years on the pill. In eight years, I hadn't missed a single one. I was very militant about it. I took one every night at six. After about five years I started to get severe migraines which the doctor attributed to the pill and put me on a progesterone-only pill instead. The migraines stopped but the progesterone gave me reflux. Not that I knew this at the time. It wasn't until we switched to condoms and my reflux improved that I made the connection. One night, drunk and dazed, we fell into bed and, as usual, when the time came, Chris reached for a condom. He spun round and showed me the inside of the box – it was empty. Fuck it, I said, and I did. We'd planned to start trying the following month anyway, so it wouldn't exactly be a disaster if we fell pregnant before then. I awoke the next morning exhilarated; we were on our way.

The doctor smiled as we entered his office and ushered us to two chairs situated opposite his desk.

'Chris and – ' he began.

'Kate,' I blurted, before he could finish.

He smiled and nodded.

'Good, good,' he said.

Chris reached out and took my hand.

'I have a medical student with me today, I hope that's okay?'

Not really, I wanted to say.

'Of course,' I said brightly, and grinned manically at the skinny kid sitting crossed-legged in the corner of the room.

'Thank you,' said the doctor. 'Simon is very interested in infertility and is thinking of specialising in it.'

Glad to be of help, I thought grimly.

'So,' the doctor began. 'You've supplied two samples, and both have come back with an absence of sperm. Correct?'

'Correct,' Chris replied.

I groaned inwardly.

'What we don't yet know,' the doctor said pushing his glasses back up his nose, 'is why.'

Simon handed the doctor a couple of sheets of A4 paper.

'The absence of sperm could be due to a mechanical problem. A blockage of some sort which is preventing the sperm from getting through. Or it could be a production problem.'

'A production problem?' I echoed, willing him on and at the same time imagining Chris' spermless sample being bottled up and shipped back by a disgruntled customer demanding a refund.

'Yes,' the doctor replied. 'It could be, though admittedly this is less likely, that Chris simply isn't making any.'

Let it be a blockage, let it be blockage.

'So where does this leave us?' Chris asked. 'More tests?'

The doctor nodded.

'I'm booking you in for a testicular ultrasound and referring you to urology. A consultant will go over the results of the ultrasound with you and take it from there.'

I blinked away tears.

'Could trauma have anything to do with this?' Chris asked suddenly.

Trauma?

'Quite possibly,' the doctor replied. He cocked his head to one side. 'Why?'

'I had to go to A&E in my first year of uni,' Chris explained. 'I had severe pain in my testicles. The doctor there treated me for testicular torsion and then discharged me.'

The doctor nodded.

'I also had some sort of op as a kid,' Chris continued. 'Undescended testicle, I think.'

The doctor looked at Simon, who yet hadn't said a word.

'Could well be a link,' he said, matter-of-factly. 'Do you happen to know which hospital carried out the op?'

Chris nodded.

'Good, good.'

The doctor smiled and leaned back in his chair.

'You'll need to contact them, probably in writing, and ask to see your records, find out exactly what you were treated for and how it all went.'

He shifted his gaze from Chris to me.

'Any questions?'

Yes, lots. But I was too frightened to ask. Luckily, Chris wasn't.

'Can a blockage be fixed?'

The doctor turned back towards Simon.

'Depends where it is and how severe it is. But most operations, I'm sorry to say, are unsuccessful,' Simon replied.

Of course they are.

'But there's always IVF,' he added, brightly.

Great.

'And if I'm not actually *making* any sperm?' Chris asked.

'Then,' the doctor said, carefully, 'you could always use a donor or foster, or adopt …'

Bile rose from my stomach and into my throat.

'But, let's not get ahead of ourselves,' he added.

It was time to go. I needed to go.

The doctor rose to his feet.

'Well,' he began, 'if there are no more questions – '

Chris shook his head and stood up to leave.

'Good, good. The hospital will be in touch with a date for your ultrasound,' he said warmly.

Chris nodded.

Simon uncrossed his legs and removed his glasses.

'Good luck,' he said, weakly, and flashed me an empty smile.

I returned his smile with a stony stare. Embarrassed, Chris grabbed my arm and ushered me quickly away.

Two days of moping and wallowing followed, but by day three, after endless Googling, I started to feel a bit better. With help, Chris and I could still be parents to our own biological children. Medical technology had moved on leaps and bounds over the last ten years and IVF success rates were improving all the time. Until we knew for sure, mourning the loss of a child-filled future was futile. Besides, right now, I had a bigger concern – Mum. I glanced at my mobile, 11 am – if I left now, I'd have the entire afternoon and evening with her. I text Dad the plan and happily prepared for the journey ahead.

CHAPTER 15

LAST CHANCE

I couldn't move. My whole body ached and tingled with pleasure. My breathing was starting to slow but my head was still spinning. Chris was lying next to me, slumped on his stomach.

'That was,' I said, breathlessly, 'absolutely bloody incredible!'

Chris nodded into his pillow. His back, lit up by a shaft of sunlight, glistened with sweat. I smiled, big and broad and wriggled up next to him. I'd just been ravished by a love God and I wanted more.

'Hey!' Chris cried out in shock as I slid my hand underneath his belly and slowly down towards his groin. He turned to face me and grabbed my hand.

'Easy,' he warned, but I couldn't be stopped. I wanted this feeling to last forever. I pulled myself up and kissed him. He tried to resist, so I kissed him harder, deeper. Chris caved, lifted me up and flipped me over. I wasn't entirely sure what had come over me. I was being driven entirely by need. I was a wild animal – hungry, determined. It had been years since I'd felt like this.

Chris collapsed beside me, panting furiously. 'That's your lot,' he said, completely done in.

I patted him on the bum. 'You were super, dahling. Just super.' I rolled over and kissed his forehead. 'I am completely, one hundred per cent, satisfied. Thank you.'

'Good,' he said, closing his eyes.

I pulled the duvet up and over us and took a couple of long deep breaths. I'd forgotten what great sex felt like. Desperate to conceive I came to think of it as a means to an end, a perfunctory task. Bored and frustrated by our lack of success I'd got bogged down in the weight of expectation and stopped enjoying it. 'Are you nearly done yet?' I'd ask midway through. 'How much longer?'

I winced at the memory. No wonder Chris had become reluctant. What man wants to hear that?! Acting on the advice of like-minded irrational women on infertility forums – I'd push him away and help the sperm in their hard-fought journey towards my egg by throwing my legs in the air, ignoring Chris completely. I shook my head, how had I let this happen? Well, never again. Chris and I couldn't conceive naturally so the pressure *attached* to the act had gone; we were free to enjoy it again. I looked over at my conked-out husband and smiled. He was sound asleep. Taking his arm and wrapping it round my waist, I quickly and happily drifted off to sleep.

I was pan frying chicken when I got the call.

'The hospital's giving up,' Ray sniffed. 'Mum's count's jumped and they're stopping the chemo.'

My heart began to thump.

'... and without the chemo,' Ray continued, her voice thin and tight, 'Dr Clarke says she'll be dead within weeks.'

I closed my eyes and sighed; we'd been here before.

'We need to prepare ourselves, apparently.'

'For what?' I asked, genuinely confused.

There was a slight pause.

'For her death.'

Anger stirred deep within me. 'Like hell we do!'

'It's over Gus. The hospital's refusing to treat her. There's nothing we can do.'

'What about that guy you emailed a couple of weeks ago?' I said.

'The specialist at The Royal Marsden?'

'Yeah.'

'I've not heard back from him.'

I bit my lip and started pacing.

'Try him again. He might have been on holiday or something.'

Ray started to cry. I kicked a kitchen cabinet dislodging a photo frame on the second shelf, sending it crashing to the floor.

'Oh Gus,' Ray whimpered, 'her little face when they told her – '

I swooped down and picked up the photo and placed it back on the shelf. It was a picture of Chris and I on our honeymoon in St Lucia. A happy, uncomplicated time, before all the madness.

'She got really upset and told him she couldn't go yet cos she needed to be around to support *you*. Dr Clarke just shook his head at her as if to say "dream on". It was horrible.'

'Bastard!'

'I know! I swear, Gus, I nearly got up and slapped him!'

'You should have done, insensitive prick.'

We needed to speak to the specialist at The Royal Marsden, right away.

'Have you got a number for that specialist?' I asked. 'I think we should call. It'll be quicker and we need to know if he can help.'

'I think so,' Ray replied. 'If not, I can find one. Shall I try now?'

I nodded furiously.

'Yes, definitely! Unless you want me to do it?'

'No, no, I'll do it,' Ray insisted, her voice becoming a little more upbeat. 'it'll give me something to do while I wait for Mum.'

The stupid chicken was stuck to the pan. I stabbed at all the bite-size chunks with a wooden spoon in an attempt to release them and turned up the heat. It'd probably taste like shit but right now, I couldn't care less. The specialist had to be able to help, he *had* to. I reached up to the top shelf to retrieve the rice. The bag was sealed. I placed it on the kitchen worktop and ripped it open. Rice exploded from the bag covering every available surface, including the floor. I shut my eyes, tore at my hair and screamed.

Mum was laughing so hard she was struggling to breathe. 'Honestly,' she gasped, 'no lie, two *completely* different shoes!'

Everybody was gawping at me in disbelief.

'How is that possible?!' Laura asked, eyeballing me.

I shrugged my shoulders.

'She did it all the time,' Mum continued, wiping a tear from her cheek with the back of her hand. 'I was always washing someone else's jumper, PE kit – '

Laura shook her head.

'Unbelievable!'

'I didn't do it on purpose!' I cried, fighting back a smile.

'I'm sure you didn't,' Laura replied, chuckling, 'but how on earth did you not notice?!'

I thought about it for a second or two.

'Too busy thinking about the next thing,' Mum suggested.

' – and too impatient to check,' added Ray.

I narrowed my eyes at her and playfully stuck out my tongue.

'Sounds about right,' Laura agreed, sniggering.

'Now hang on a minute,' Mum said, coming to my defence. 'Like Kate says, she didn't do it on purpose, and,' Mum looked at me and gave me a little wink, 'it certainly kept me amused.'

It really was quite staggering how many times I arrived home from school in someone else's jumper. I didn't see it as a major problem at the time, a jumper's a jumper. My school uniform wasn't important to me, so I treated it carelessly. I'd leave it on the changing room floor to get trampled on, and not bother to check if it was the same one after my lesson. Instead, I'd quickly get changed and carry on with my day. Plus, iced buns were sold at break time and if you didn't get in line quickly you didn't get one. It was simple really – if something's important it gets my full attention, if it isn't, it doesn't. As an adult this attitude often gets me in trouble. I threw away Chris' driving licence a couple of years ago. I'd been on at him for weeks to sort out his 'pile of crap' on the dining room table. I like surfaces clean and clutter free and looking at it every day really started to get to me. So, one afternoon, without checking through the pile, I scooped the whole lot up and dumped it. A couple of days later, after the bin men had come and gone, Chris stormed up to me demanding to know what I'd done with his pile of stuff.

'Dumped it,' I said, matter-of-factly.

Chris balled his fists and thumped the door frame. 'Great!' he'd fumed. 'Just great! My driving licence was in that pile!'

Whoops. I tried to defend my actions. 'You shouldn't have left it there,' I argued. 'It should've been filed away somewhere safe.'

'I was getting round to it. It didn't need to be done asap! You shouldn't just chuck stuff out without checking just because it's offending you or because you're too impatient to wait for me to sort it,' Chris shot back. He was right of course, but at the time I insisted it was as much his fault as mine.

Laura glanced at her watch.

'Shouldn't the nurse be here by now?'

'I'll go and see what's keeping her,' said Dad, getting to his feet.

The five of us were all sitting around Mum's bed at The Royal Marsden Hospital. She'd had an assessment a couple of days ago and been admitted for intensive chemo. After speaking to Ray on the phone the specialist at the hospital, Mr David Green, disagreed with Dr Clarke that nothing more could be done and had invited Mum for an assessment the very next day. His conclusion: cycle three had had a positive effect and Mum was definitely strong enough to withstand more treatment. It was a huge relief. We were warned her situation was 'grave' and the chemo 'unlikely to work' but it was another chance, her last chance, and if Mum wanted to carry on fighting, then so did we.

The car in front of me was just a metre or so ahead. A little more pressure on the accelerator and I'd crash straight into the boot. It was tempting. I didn't want to crash and die, but a few days in intensive care would give me a reprieve and hopefully when I came round it'd all be better. I shook the thought from my mind, gripped the steering wheel and forced myself to concentrate. It was a stupid thought. I'd be no use to anyone in intensive care, but after months and months of rollercoaster living, cracks were beginning to show. I was snappy, joyless and irritable at work and fed up and uncommunicative at home. My last two periods had been especially painful; it was like my womb was punishing me, annoyed and frustrated at having released yet *another* unfertilised egg.

Before I knew it, I was just a couple of turnings away from The Royal Marsden. It was Friday; I'd last visited at the weekend. Mum was in good spirits but suffering from a very itchy rash brought on by the antibiotics she'd been given for an 'unexplained infection'. It was a blessing in disguise as Mum was very quickly moved out of the communal ward and into her own private room to prevent the infection from spreading to other patients. Ray had set up her iPod and later, in the evening, while taking it turns to rub her neck and back – the worst affected areas – we settled down to watch *Strictly*.

Midweek, Laura called with an update. Mum was doing well, and the doctors were happy with how everything was progressing. Today or Monday we'd be given her count. I found a parking space, made myself presentable and walked towards the entrance of the hospital.

'How many letters?'

I looked back down at the grid and counted.

'Ten altogether, but it's divided into three words – three, two and five. The last letter of the first word is a T and the second letter of the third word is an H.'

Mum curled her thumb and fingers around her chin.

' – and the clue?'

'Unfit.'

'Hmmm,' Mum mused, relaxing back into her pillows. 'Something of or something at – '

'Out of shape!' I shouted and almost leapt off my chair.

Mum threw her hands up in the air.

'Of course!'

'Yay!' I squealed, scribbling in the final word. 'We've done it, we've completed it!'

'*You* did it,' Mum corrected with a smile.

'True,' I crowed, 'but *you* usually get the final clue, so it was about time!'

Mum enjoyed crosswords and was good at them. She insisted it wasn't really a skill, more a way of thinking. Practise makes perfect, she said, and it was true. Mum and I had done our fair share of crosswords over the years, and I'd definitely improved.

'You know,' Mum said, plucking a juicy red grape from a bowl on her side table, 'some of the stories in here are truly horrific.'

I cocked my head to one side, urging her to continue.

'There's a woman next door who is fighting a brain tumour. It's her third cancer and her consultant is doubtful she'll beat it. She's got three sons for goodness' sake, all under ten.'

'Christ, that's awful.'

'I know,' Mum agreed. 'How unfair is that?'

'How's she coping?'

'Not brilliantly, she mostly just sits in bed and stares out the window. Her partner was here the other day – neither of them said a word.'

Mum reached out and squeezed my hand.

'At least you're all grown up and well equipped to deal with world.'

I wasn't so sure about that.

'*You're* healthy, remember that.'

How did she do that? How did she know what I was thinking about and know exactly what to say? I lowered my eyes and nodded.

'Your father called a couple of fertility clinics last week and asked about your options.' I very nearly fell off my chair.

'He did?!'

Mum nodded.

'– and it all sounds really positive.'

I looked up at her and smiled.

'Well, it's all on the back burner for the time being. You're – '

My mobile started to ring. It was Chris.

'Hey.'

'Guess what?'

'What?'

'I got it!'

'Got what?'

'The job! The job at Rolls-Royce! I start in November.'

'Crikey,' I managed.

'We agreed I'd take it if I got it, right?'

Had we?

'Yes, of course,' I said, unconvincingly. 'It's what you've always wanted.'

'You sure?'

No.

'Absolutely!'

'Great!'

This wasn't a conversation I could continue.

'Listen,' I said, sounding brighter and more assured than I felt, 'I've gotta go, I'm with Mum; we'll talk about it when I get home, okay?'

'Of course,' Chris replied. 'Give her my love.'

'Will do.'

I snapped shut my phone and slumped back in my chair.

'Chris got the job at Rolls-Royce.'

'The one in Derby?'

'The one in Derby.'

'Oh.'

Yeah, oh.

'He's always wanted to work there – '

' – but what about you?'

'I can't deny him. It wouldn't be fair.' I broke eye contact and gazed out the window. 'Derby's not so far away,' I said.

Mum pulled a face.

'You never know,' I continued, 'I might like it.'

'You might.'

At that moment a freakishly tall man with a swan-like neck walked into the room and pulled up a chair beside me. 'Afternoon Sally,' he said, looking directly at Mum, 'and how are you today?'

Mum beamed up at him.

'Good thanks, Giles.'

Giles? I'd never seen or heard of him. Mum introduced us.

'This is my consultant, Kate. Giles, this is my middle daughter, Kate.'

I stretched out my hand.

'Hi.'

He took it and shook it, hard.

'Hi.'

'So,' Mum began, 'am I free to go?'

Giles nodded.

'You most certainly are!'

'So, my count's okay?'

Giles paused and scratched his head.

'It's okay, but it's a little higher than we'd like.'

'Oh.'

'It's not bad,' Giles added. 'And it's nothing to be alarmed about. It's common to see a small rise like this. It's the body readjusting after chemo. What we don't want is for the count to get any higher.'

Mum looked as confused as I felt.

'Go home, enjoy your weekend, and we'll test again first thing Monday.'

'I can stay,' I offered after Giles had left. I was due back in Oxford at six for a party. I wasn't really sure I wanted to go, but Chris thought it would be good for me, so I'd agreed.

'No, no, your father will be here soon. In fact,' Mum glanced up at the clock, 'he should be here *now*!'

We both knew it wasn't Dad's lateness that was bothering her.

'You heard what he said Mum – a small rise is expected. Put it out of your mind.'

'It didn't rise after cycle three.'

'Not straight away, no, but when it did, it rose with a vengeance. This could be how a successful cycle is *supposed* to go. Giles didn't seem worried.'

Mum thought about this for a while.

'True, true.'

Dad breezed through the door a couple of minutes later clutching a bag of chocolate buttons.

'You're late,' Mum snapped.

'Am I?'

'Yes, you know you are. Where have you been?'

'I was just around the corner visiting a mate.'

Mum glared at him.

'You were supposed to be here at three.'

'It's not a problem, I – ' I began.

Mum cut me off.

'Yes, it is! You've a party to get to – your father knew this.'

'It's not a big deal, honestly.'

Mum said it *was* a big deal and ordered Dad to apologise. After he'd said sorry, and admitted that he'd forgotten, I got up to leave and reluctantly said my goodbyes. Mum did her best to convince me that she was fine even though we both knew she wasn't. Damn it! Thursday, my last working day, couldn't come soon enough. Just five more days, I told myself on the way out, and I'd finally be free.

CHAPTER 16

BIRTHDAY

You'd think you'd get used to hearing bad news, but you don't. Monday's call was just as unbearable as all the others. In fact, it was worse. The chemo had failed, big time. Mum's count was sky high. Nothing more could be done. The leukaemia had won. The consultants sent Mum home with a drug that they hoped would contain it, but she'd never be free of it and the disease that we'd all fought so hard to beat would eventually kill her.

The drug was in liquid form and needed to be injected daily. Ray was taught how to do it and to make it all a little easier for her we all agreed that a temporary move to Dad's flat was an absolute must. Ray packed her bags and left her London home that very afternoon. How long she'd be needed was a complete unknown.

Mum remained upbeat believing she'd still get her 'miracle' but for the rest of us, it was almost impossible. The rug had been ripped from under us so many times, why believe this time would be any different? We didn't let on, of course, and although hope was fading it *was* still flickering, and until it had been snuffed out completely, we owed it to Mum and ourselves to remain strong and optimistic. So, Monday evening, after work, I headed for the shops. It was Mum's birthday Saturday and I needed to buy her a present. I raided the rails in a dozen or so outlets before settling on a deep blue capped-sleeve tunic. It was fitted and fell just above the knee. She'd look cute in it I decided and quickly paid for it before I changed my mind.

By close of play Thursday, I was so desperate to go I left my digital radio behind; my boss texted me as soon as I got home. 'Keep it,' I said. 'I can easily pick up another one.' I shouldn't have just given it away like that, it had been a gift to me when I left my job as a reporter at a big commercial radio station and would be hard to replace. But at that precise moment I was so damn relieved to be outta there I wasn't really thinking straight. It was a rash decision and one I'd rue in the months ahead.

I called Mum as soon as I got home and told her I'd be over tomorrow, at about midday. She sounded flat and distant. I asked her what was wrong. Pain, she said, just below her left ribs, she'd been up all night and was knackered; come Saturday, she advised. I agreed, but I was far from happy about it. Why was she in pain? Why hadn't Ray told me? A lot had changed since I'd last seen Mum and I was champing at the bit to get to her. To pass the time I decided to bake a birthday cake. I'd never made one before. I looked up a lemon drizzle cake recipe online, printed it off and set to work. Ray called Friday afternoon and said she was taking Mum to a recommended reiki practitioner many miles away in Bournemouth. Mum was still in pain and remembering the success of her first reiki experience in Devon, Ray thought it might help. I couldn't think of any valid reason to disagree, other than it would prevent me from seeing Mum until the evening, which was very much my issue, not Mum's. So, I told Ray to go ahead. Laura suggested we spruce up the flat while they were out so that it'd be clean and sparkly when they returned. Mum moaned regularly about the state of the flat, and Laura thought it'd be a good opportunity to clean it properly, as well as help to alleviate our bubbling anxiety.

We arrived at the flat mid-afternoon. Laura retrieved a huge bag of cleaning products from the boot of her car and handed me a bucket and mop.

'Dad's will be crap,' she reasoned.

We climbed the communal staircase and let ourselves in. Wilf greeted us with his usual boundless enthusiasm, but with no treats on offer and a walk out of the question he quickly retreated to his bed and left us to it.

'Here,' said Laura, handing me a toothbrush, 'use this.'

I furrowed my brow.

'It's brilliant at removing limescale,' she explained. 'I do it all the time.'

Crikey, Laura intended to tackle *everything*!

'You don't do things by half do you?' I teased.

Laura laughed, 'Nope.'

'But do you really think it's worth the bother? Is anyone going to notice?'

'Mum will,' Laura replied, matter-of-factly.

I couldn't argue with that; Mum missed nothing.

' – and after that?'

Laura pointed at the coffee table.

'Dust, and don't forget the legs.'

'Yes Sir!' I said, snapping out a salute.

Laura walked over to the sound system.

'Queen?' she suggested.

'Defo' I agreed.

We needed some help to keep us going, and Freddie, as always, could be relied upon to provide it.

'Wow,' said Ray, walking into the flat. 'It looks amazing!'

'Should bloody well hope so,' I replied, smiling. 'We've been at it for ages!'

Laura rushed over to the coffee table and picked up the remote.

'*Strictly*'s about to start!' she said, turning on the TV.

'Mum's not feeling great, she's really tired,' Ray said. 'I don't think the reiki helped at all. She's barely said a word.'

'Where is she?' asked Laura, muting the TV.

'Dad's helping her up the stairs. She's got zilch energy,' Ray said.

Laura and I exchanged worried glances.

'What about the pain?' I asked, 'under her ribs?'

'Still there, I'm going to give her a shot of oxycodone in a minute.'

'Is that the painkiller that works a bit like morphine?' Laura asked.

Ray nodded.

'I've given it to her for the last two days; I don't think it's having much of an effect though.'

Why was she in so much pain? And needing help getting up

the stairs? I swallowed, hard.

Mum and Dad finally emerged; their arms tightly linked. Dad led her slowly into the lounge where the three of us were waiting.

'Happy birthday!' we sang out in unison.

Mum looked at all three of us, her eyes sad and moist.

'Thank you,' she squeaked.

Dad guided her to the sofa and arranged the cushions behind her.

'Comfortable?' he asked.

Mum nodded, weakly.

'What can I get you?'

'Earl Grey, please,' she said.

Ray breezed into the room carrying a small tray.

'Time for your shot,' she said, positioning herself next to Mum on the arm of the sofa.

Mum rolled up her sleeve and Ray stabbed her.

'There,' she said, dabbing the injection site with a piece of cotton wool, 'all done.'

Mum smiled at her and looked at the TV. *Strictly* was still on but had been all but forgotten.

'Turn it up,' Mum said.

Ray and I looked at the screen.

'Such a lovely figure, why can't they dress her properly? Her boobs are all squished in,' Mum said.

'I know!' I agreed, laughing. 'Laura and I reckon the head of wardrobe's got it in for her and dresses her badly on purpose.'

Mum let out a little laugh. Perhaps she wasn't as bad as we all feared?

'Dinner's ready!' Laura announced, placing plates of food on Dad's coffee table. She smiled, turned and went to fetch the rest.

We ate our dinner, huddled around the TV, commenting on the dances, and making score predictions as usual. All of us, except Mum. She occasionally looked up and smiled but that was it. She stopped eating halfway through the programme and stared vacantly towards the window. I forced my attention back on the TV, stealing glances at her every couple of minutes to see if she'd resumed eating.

Laura and I cleared away the plates and put half a dozen candles in the cake I'd made and made our way back into the lounge. Laura dimmed the lights and started singing.

'Make a wish,' I said, when the singing stopped.

Mum sighed heavily and obliged. I returned to the kitchen, cut five equal slices and told myself to calm down. Nothing to worry about, she was just tired. Mum refused a slice at first, changing her mind only after Dad had told her it had been made by me.

'Spots,' Mum said quietly. 'I can see spots. Lots and lots of little red spots.'

'Spots?' Laura motioned for Dad to mute the TV.

'You alright, love?' Dad asked, shuffling over to her on his knees.

Mum didn't respond. Dad picked up my present.

'The girls have got you some presents,' Dad said, cheerily. 'Why don't you open them?'

Mum blinked and a solitary tear rolled down her cheek.

She took the parcel and slowly unwrapped it. She took out the dress, held it up into the light and smiled.

'It's lovely,' she said, inspecting it closely from all angles.

Ray nodded.

'It really is. Good buy, Gus!'

'Glad you both like it,' I replied, trying to supress my building anxiety.

Mum folded the garment and carelessly placed it on the arm of the chair. Not good; Mum didn't discard clothes, thoughtlessly. Every purchase – bought or given as a gift – was cleaned and ironed and carefully hung up as though it were a rare and highly prized ancient relic.

'Thank you,' she whispered, before returning her gaze to the window.

Dad picked up another bundle off the floor.

You've got another one here – '

Laura shook her head, silently urging him to stop.

' – from Laura,' he continued, handing it to Mum.

Laura glared at him. But still Dad ignored her.

'Shall I help you unwrap it?' he pressed.

Mum turned her head back towards us but made no attempt to respond. Dad unwrapped the present.

'Ooh,' Dad cooed, holding up a camel-coloured cardigan, 'it's beautiful,' he said rubbing it against his cheek, 'and it's really soft.'

Mum reached out to touch it.

'It'll look lovely with the blue dress Kate got you.'

Dad was on a roll; it was excruciating.

'Thank you, girls,' Mum said, weakly.

'You're welcome,' I replied, feeling sick to my stomach.

Mum shivered and Dad instinctively rubbed her arm. It was covered in goose pimples. The heating was on. It wasn't cold. Fuck. Dad, still holding the cardigan, suggested she wear it. Mum didn't respond. Dad gently draped it over her shoulders. This was hideous. What the hell was she thinking? Why wasn't she saying anything? Laura, Ray and I, upset and confused, exchanged glances. It was frightening; we'd never seen Mum like this before. It was like she'd switched herself off. Laura rose to her feet and marched to the coat rack.

'I'm going to have to go,' she announced, reluctantly, tears pooling in her eyes, and hugged and kissed us all goodbye.

'How about a film?' Dad suggests a little while later.

'Sure,' I say, without enthusiasm.

Halfway through the film Mum says she's in pain and asks Ray for more oxycodone. As soon as the credits start to roll Dad offers to help Mum get ready for bed, but she refuses.

'I'm staying here,' she says, stubbornly.

Ray gets her a pillow and a duvet while I brush my teeth and get changed into my pyjamas. Dad and Ray kiss Mum goodnight and retreat to their bedrooms. My bed for the night is a two-man sofa. I quietly and reluctantly climb into it, fluff my pillow and look over at Mum; she's already asleep, her head lolled to one side, her mouth slightly ajar. I sigh. Sleep for me would take a while. Dad's flat was on a busy high street, above his old shop and studio. It was noisy, and a streetlamp, directly outside the lounge window, flickered incessantly, like an excitable puppy desperate for attention.

I nodded off at about half two in the morning, only to be awoken by heavy, laboured, breathing. What the hell?! I looked nervously around me, clutched the duvet to my chest and sat up in horror as my eyes reached a hunched, shadowy figure by the lounge door. Mum was shuffling towards me like an evil old witch in a Disney film. I stayed perfectly still; eyes fixed on her. She finally reached the chair she'd been sleeping in and lowered herself into it. Christ, it'd taken her over five minutes to walk across a room a little over 12-foot wide! This was bad. Really, really bad.

CHAPTER 17

TOUCH AND GO

I'd been awake for about fifteen minutes, but I couldn't bring myself to turn around and look at the chair where Mum had fallen asleep. Perhaps it had all been a bad dream. I pushed myself up onto my elbows and turned my head to face her. Mum was staring blankly out of the window, her hand trembling by her mouth. I threw the duvet to one side and dropped to a crouch beside her.

'Mum?'

She slowly turned towards me and squinted, hard.

'Mum?' I said again, worry whirring frantically inside me.

I took her hand in mine and started stroking it.

'Are you okay?

Mum cocked her head to one side, searched my face and rested her gaze just past my eyes. Why wasn't she looking at me properly? I swallowed hard and failed to hold back the tears that trickled silently down my face. My nose started to run, and I sniffed.

'Have you got a cold, darling?'

A cold? Couldn't she see that I was crying? Shit. She couldn't see; that's why she wasn't looking at me properly. Mum winced.

'Where does it hurt?' I asked.

She pointed to the same spot under her ribs.

'I'll get Ray,' I said, but just as I was about to get up, she walked cautiously into the lounge and gave me a look as if to say, 'is everything okay?'

I shook my head and squeezed Mum's hand.

'Mum,' I croaked, dreading the answer to the question I was about to ask her. 'Can you see me?'

More squinting.

'Sort of,' she said softly. 'I know it's you, but I can't really make out any of your features.'

'Red spots?' asked Ray, leaning on the back of the sofa and looking directly at Mum.

'Mmmm,' Mum nodded. 'Lots of them,' she said, turning her head back to the window.

Ray's eyes fill with tears. 'Mum needs a shot of oxycodone,' I tell her. I ask Mum if she wants a drink. She does – Earl Grey. I shout at Ray to put the kettle on.

It's 9 am. Dad stumbles into the lounge yawning and tying his dressing gown. He drops to his knees beside Mum.

'Alright kiddo?'

Mum's face crumples. Dad pulls her to him and gently rocks her.

'Aw, baby,' he coos.

Mum pushes him away.

'I can't see!' she cries, hands fixed to her face.

Dad's head snaps back in alarm.

'You can't see?'

She shakes her head and collapses into him. Dad shoots me a look – his eyes wide with panic.

'I need the toilet,' Mum announces a little while later.

She tries to get up, but she can't. Dad offers her his forearms, tells her to grip on hard and pulls her to her feet. Arm in arm they make their way to the bathroom. I look on in horror; Mum can barely lift her feet. Dad switches his position and guides her from the front, taking both of her hands, gently steering her towards him. Every now and again he glances up at me, his face a twisted mess of pain and fear. It breaks my heart. Who *was* this woman and what the hell had she done with my Mum?! Why couldn't she see? And why was she in so much pain? Just last week we'd been chatting and laughing as usual.

Dad guided Mum back into the lounge and settled her into her chair. Ray handed her a mug of tea and sat down beside me. The trip to the loo had finished her off. Her breathing was slow and ragged; her body limp and trembling with exhaustion. What to do? Hospital, we agreed. We had to get her to hospital.

An ambulance arrived thirty minutes later. Two paramedics rush through the door, and after a few questions, quickly and carefully lift Mum from her chair and strap her into whatever it was they'd brought in with them. They talk to her the entire time. Mum says nothing. I look on, disbelieving. It's like a scene from *Casualty* They carry her down two flights of stairs, cleverly shielding her from potential knocks, and out into the rain-soaked street below: me, Ray and Dad trailing nervously behind. Locals stop and gawp as the paramedics load her into the ambulance. I want to scream at them, 'Fuck off!' This wasn't a show; it was real life, *my* life! I climb into the back of the ambulance, anger racing and raging inside of me, and sit down beside her. Was this it? Would it all end here? The engine started. We'd be at the hospital in twenty-five minutes. I took Mum's hand and silently wept the entire way there.

The paramedics park Mum next to a bed in the AML ward and leave. She's slumped in her chair like a rag doll, head lolled to one side, eyes fixed to the floor. Dad and Ray arrive.

'What's happening?' Ray asks, looking about frantically.

'Nothing,' I reply, chewing my cheek. 'The paramedics dumped her here and left. We've seen no one.'

Ten minutes later a nurse walks in and the four of us transfer Mum into an empty bed, Ray fluffing and sorting the pillows. Mum's unresponsive to questioning and the nurse flees. A doctor, she assures us, will drop by shortly. Dad finds a couple of chairs in the corridor outside the ward, and we sit and wait.

A doctor arrives thirty minutes later. He's young and overweight. He shines a light in Mum's eyes and examines the area under her ribs. Mum groans.

'What's wrong with her?' asks Ray.

'Hard to say,' the doctor replies. 'She's either had a bleed or leukemic blasts have clumped together behind her eyes, which is why she can't see. As for the pain,' he continued, 'I think it's her spleen – it's very common in patients with AML.'

'Her breathing is slow and laboured.'

The doctor turns in my direction and gives a quick nod of his head.

'I would imagine she's got a low HB. I'll get one of the nurses to take some blood.'

Mum looks up at Dad and asks for some water. Bollocks. The nurse who left us and fetched the doctor had also promised to return with a fresh jug. She'd clearly forgotten. Dad muttered something incoherent and marched off to find her. Mum, let out a little moan and reached out for my hand.

'Oh Kate,' she said, quietly, searching my face.

'I'm here,' I assure her, inching a little closer and stroking the top of her head.

Her HB is dangerously low; hooked up to various machines, nurses start pumping her full of fluids and painkillers. 'It'll help make her more comfortable,' we're told.

Mum drifts in and out of consciousness all afternoon while we sat and stared. At nothing. At each other. At the floor. There was nothing any of us could do but leaving was out of the question. We attempted conversation.

'Are you looking forward to moving to Derby?' Dad asked.

'I've started singing in a contemporary choir,' Laura informed us. 'It's all very laid back and informal; the conductor's lots of fun,' she looked at me and smiled. 'You'd be great at it.'

A little while later, Laura checks out the communal visitors' lounge. 'We could sleep in shifts,' she suggests. 'The chairs are a lot comfier in there.'

I didn't like the idea; what if something happened and I was in another room? Mum sits up and howls out in pain. We buzz for help. A sweet-looking male nurse appears.

'Where does it hurt, Sally?' he asks.

'I don't fucking know,' Mum spits at him. 'It just hurts!'

Mum's outburst is a shock, but the nurse takes it in his stride, gently examining her to locate the pain. He administers more painkillers and updates her medical file. Mum soon settles and even starts snoring. The nurse asks if we were staying. We all nod.

The night is long and restless. We try everything we can think of to achieve sleep – making pillows out of jumpers and cardigans and resting our heads or feet at the foot of Mum's bed, but nothing works. The task is made more difficult by the sounds of all the medical machinery. It is cold too. In the early hours I give up completely and doodle on the window instead. Mum wakes briefly at about three.

'Why are you all here?' she asks, but before I could answer she's drifted back to sleep.

Morning finally arrives. We look at each other's creased faces and laugh.

'Wow,' said Laura, staring disapprovingly at her reflection in the window.

I rubbed my eyes, yawned and stretched out my legs.

'It's a good job Mum can't see, eh?'

Laura let out a sad little laugh.

'Certainly is,' she agreed and dived into her handbag for her toothbrush.

As she was about to up and leave, a pretty, middle-aged nurse walked in, acknowledged us with a smile and began changing Mum's fluid bag.

'Did you stay here all night?' she asks.

'Yep,' I reply.

The nurse nods her head, impressed.

'Feel free to use the nurses' changing room if you want to freshen up a bit.'

Grateful for the offer, we all smiled and thanked her.

Ten minutes or so later, a doctor arrived.

'How's she doing?' he asked us, while feeling her forehead.

'Slept the night whole night through,' I inform him.

The doctor glanced at the machines, removed a notepad from his pocket, scribbled something down, returned the notepad to his pocket and took a couple of steps back.

'We weren't sure she'd make it,' he said, in a hushed and gentle tone.

I look up at him, puzzled.

'She was in a very bad way,' he admitted, 'just a few – '

'We could have lost her?!' I butt in, fighting back tears.

'Quite possibly,' the doctor nodded.

I slump back in my chair. Fuck. I knew it was bad, but I hadn't realised it was *that* bad.

'She's a real fighter,' the doctor said with a smile.

'So, what now?' Laura asked, matter-of-factly.

The doctor shifted his weight awkwardly from one foot to the other.

'We keep her here, for monitoring, and take it from there.'

Laura took a deep breath and looked directly at him.

'How long?' she croaked.

His reply was clipped and mechanical.

'Not long – a week, two at most. All we can do now is keep her as comfortable as possible, whether that be here or at home.'

The room started to sway. I clutched onto the sides of my chair and fought the urge to hurl. It was over. My beautiful, vibrant Mum had survived the night but would be dead within days. I jumped out of my chair, marched angrily to the toilet, and crumpled into a sad and sobbing heap on the floor.

CHAPTER 18

TALK TO ME

'It's a no-brainer,' Laura said, emphatically. 'Devon.'

'I'm not sure she's up to it,' argued Dad. 'And surely, she's safer here with all the nurses and so on?'

'I'm with Laura,' I agreed. 'She always said her biggest nightmare was dying bald in a cancer ward – '

'And we'd all be with her,' Ray added, 'taking care of her, keeping her comfortable. It's what she'd want.'

Dad looked far from convinced.

'I don't know, I think the move will cause her too much stress.'

Rubbish.

'This is Mum we're talking about,' I reminded him. 'She'll probably hang on till Christmas, defy us all and achieve the unthinkable – remission. We *have* to go back to Devon.'

'And don't forget,' Ray began, 'the doctor said they would do whatever was necessary to get her back home.'

'That's correct, Sir,' said a willowy woman with bright pink lipstick. 'We will pump her full of pain-relief and sedatives – she'll be completely comfortable and unaware of the journey.'

We'd been sat with this woman for well over half an hour. She was a 'discharge co-ordinator' or something like that. She'd set up a meeting with us to discuss the pros and cons of home and hospital deaths: a jolly job. She edged a little closer to me and I wished she hadn't; her breath reeked of coffee. I discreetly moved my hand up to my face.

'You should know,' she began, in an overly sympathetic tone, 'and I'm sorry that it has to be brought up, that if you *do* decide to go back to Devon the paramedics on board the ambulance will not interfere should something happen on the way. If Sally stopped breathing, for example, she would not be resuscitated.'

'Why not?' asked Dad, leaning forward, eyes blazing.

'Standard procedure for end-of-life patients.'

End-of-life patients. So that's what she was now; a woman on the brink of death; no hope of survival; a lost cause.

'Because?' Dad pressed.

The woman rattled out a routine response.

'To prevent unnecessary suffering, Sir. Resuscitation can cause broken ribs, fractures, a ruptured spleen, brain damage … it would not be in Sally's best interest.'

Dad sat back in his chair, rubbing his chin.

'So,' said the woman, taking us all in. 'Have we reached a decision? Or do you need more time?'

It was three against one. Dad scratched his head, stood up and crossed his arms.

'Devon. The girls are right; it's what Sally would want.'

The woman nodded, clutched the papers she was holding to her chest and stood up.

'A pleasure to meet you all,' she said with a smile that revealed lipstick-stained teeth.

'I'll get the ball rolling.'

We all nodded, thanked her and bid her farewell.

Mum was stable and out of pain but apart from gesturing at the water jug every now and then she was still and silent. I wasn't sure if she *couldn't* speak, or if she was choosing not to. She got herself into a bit of a panic when the nurses moved her into a private room.

'Where am I going?' she wailed, eyes wide and frantic. 'You're taking me somewhere to die, aren't you! I don't want to go, girls!'

The nurses attempted to calm her. 'We're taking you to your own room, to give you more privacy. It's all okay, nothing to worry about.' We dutifully followed, heads heavy and low. Ray set up Mum's iPod and docking station in the hope that some music might bring her back to us; it didn't. She gazed up at the ceiling and dozed in and out of sleep.

Later that afternoon a nurse we'd never seen before walked into the room and began changing Mum's fluid bag. The process took about twenty minutes; irreverent chit-chat was inevitable.

'You girl's alright?'

Laura shrugged.

The nurse pulled a sympathetic face.

'Do you all live locally?'

We answered one by one.

'Kids? she asked.

I shook my head.

'Three boys,' said Laura.

The nurse's eyes lit up like a Christmas tree.

'I've four! Three boys, one girl.'

Laura's eyebrows shot up.

'We really wanted a girl, so we tried one last time … you're not tempted?'

Laura laughed and shook her head.

'Noooo – three's enough for me!'

And that was it; they were off. They discussed it all – labour, discipline, behavioural differences, blah, blah, bloody blah. It went on and on. I might as well have been invisible. For the first time in my life, I'd been shut out and I had no way in. I wasn't a mother so what did I know? What could I say or add that could possibly be of any interest? I knew nothing of the pain and drudgery of breastfeeding and even less about the trials and tribulations of child rearing – and I probably never would. I'd have to put up with conversations like these again and again for the rest of my life. I felt like the school geek – denied acceptance and admittance by the cool and popular gang for being different; for failing to comply. Women with kids would forever ignore and pity me. Too confusing a prospect, they'd cast me adrift and forget me. Motherhood – a secret, sacred sect I was unlikely ever to be a part of. I forced a smile, but in truth, never in my entire life had I felt more alone, worthless and irrelevant.

'Kate?' It was Mum; she sounded concerned. Nothing wrong with her ears then. I reached for her hand and gently squeezed it, 'right here,' I said softly. Mum smiled and closed her eyes. A single tear rolled down my cheek; still looking out for me, I thought.

Mum's silence was driving us all mad! It was becoming unbearable. Why wasn't she talking to any of us? Mum *always* had something to say. Was she scared? Had she given up? We had absolutely no idea and it was making us all a little stir crazy. Mum was the captain of our family ship; without her we were rudderless and adrift.

By day three I'd finally had enough. Mum's breathing had become frighteningly unsteady; the pauses in between each breath were too long. Ray, hand clasped to her mouth, fled the room. I followed her.

'I can't just sit there and watch her die, Gus!'

'I know, I know,' I soothed.

'I keep thinking I'm witnessing her last breath – I can't watch that; I just can't.'

Ray turned on her heel and ran towards the double doors at the end of the corridor. I leaned against the wall and sighed: time to take action. There was absolutely no way she was going to die without talking to us. I would *force* her to talk; force her to engage. It's what we did. Her body may be broken but *she* wasn't. There was stuff to say, stuff to know. I returned to Mum's room with a renewed sense of purpose and calmly asked Dad to leave. He looked at me, unsure.

'Please?' I said, looking at him long and hard.

'Okay,' he said eventually. 'I'll be right outside.'

I lowered myself into the chair Dad had vacated and picked up and squeezed Mum's hand. My heart started to thump. Calm down, I told myself and took a long, deep breath. Mum always responded when I needed her; it was obvious what to say.

'Mum?' I closed my eyes and squeezed again. 'I'm scared.'

Her face twitched.

'I don't know what I'm going to do without you. I – I – '

I couldn't continue. Tears filled my eyes and splashed onto the back of Mum's hand. She couldn't see me, but she could hear me and feel me. She turned towards me.

'Oh Kate-kins,' she whimpered, her big, wet eyes searching for my face, 'I'm scared too.'

And that was it; the floodgates were well and truly open.

'I love you so much,' I sniffed.

'I love you too!'

'How are you feeling? What are you thinking?'

'Nothing.'

'Nothing?!'

'Well, apart from how unfair this all is and how hard it's going to be for you all,' her voice caught in her throat, 'when I'm gone.'

'Don't worry about that,' I replied, fobbing her off.

Mum's voice slowed and lowered.

'I've been there Kate; I know what it's like.'

There was no fooling Mum; not even now, so I stopped pretending.

'Shit, Mum, what am I going to do?!' The fear and desperation I'd buried deep within me rose with alarming speed. 'My future's a mess. Do you think I'll be alright? Should I have IVF? What's the point in me having kids if *you're* not going to see them?!'

'Nonsense!' Mum barked. 'Take advantage of all the medical channels open to you. You were born to be a mother and a mother you *will* be.'

'But what if – '

'It'll happen, Kate, and when it does, you'll know *exactly* what to do.'

Mum's cheeks were as wet as mine.

'I wish I had more to show for my life; given you more to be proud of – '

'Kate, good God! I am *so* proud of you; you have no idea! You have given me nothing but pleasure. You've accomplished so much!' Mum reached out and touched my cheek, 'and as a person,' she continued, 'you blow me away.'

I leant over and kissed her on the forehead. Mum's brow wrinkled.

'I worry about Ray the most.'

'No need,' I assured her. 'Ray is more wise and more capable than any of us have ever given her credit for.'

'Oh, I know that; I've always known that. I just wish she'd believe in herself a bit more; like herself a bit more – she's so self-destructive.'

I inched a little closer. I wanted her to hear me, fully.

'I'll always do what I can, Mum, I promise.'

She smiled.

'I'm not scared of dying,' she said suddenly. 'Honestly. I'm scared for all of *you*. It's always worse for the ones who are left behind.'

Relief and joy flooded through me; Mum was back; she was alive, and she was talking. Ray needed to hear this as much as me.

'Don't say another word,' I ordered. 'I'll be right back.'

I shot up, burst through the door and raced down the corridor to find Ray.

I quickly reached the top of a flight of stairs and eagerly pushed through a pair of double doors. Ray was one flight down clutching a cup of tea.

'Ray!' I shouted.

Ray froze in panic and the colour drained from her face.

'No, no,' I laughed, adrenaline swirling around my bloodstream. 'it's okay, everything's okay. Mum's talking!'

Ray stared at me, bemused.

'Now!' I demanded, 'Hurry!'

Ray charged up the stairs, handed me her piping hot tea and sped off down the corridor towards Mum. I left them to it. I'd had my moment; it was Ray's turn.

Sometimes, I mused, while walking slowly back to Mum's room, you just have to bite the bullet, trust your instincts and take control; force a situation to arise. Mum needed and wanted to talk just as much as we needed and wanted to *hear* her talk. She was as lost as we were; after all what use is a captain without its crew? I smiled and happily re-entered Mum's room; together, as ever, was the only way forward.

CHAPTER 19

BACK TO DEVON

'You're kidding, right?!'

Chris shrugged.

'You said to bring a selection – '

I cut him off.

'Of outfits that I actually wear – '

An old, faded orange Levi Strauss T-shirt caught my eye. I pulled it out of the bag and held it up, 'Seriously?!'

'I like that T-shirt,' Chris said, matter-of-factly.

'So did I!' I exclaimed, 'back in 1999!'

He shrugged again.

'Sorry.'

I felt a pang of guilt. Chris had done exactly what I'd asked, and he'd done it quickly. 'Just stuff lots of different bits and bobs in a bag and bring it to me,' I'd said to him earlier. 'I don't care what.'

He'd driven to the hospital straight from work and was heading straight back; three hours driving in total, and here I was criticising him.

'No,' I began, and leaned over to kiss him. '*I'm* sorry.' I buried my face in my hands. 'I'm all over the place.'

Placing the bag of clothes on the floor, he pulled me towards him for a hug. I started to cry.

'I can't believe it's all over. How can it all be over?'

Chris said nothing; just rocked and stroked me.

'I've no idea when I'll next see you,' I said. 'It could be weeks! And when I do Mum will be – '

I pulled away and wiped my cheeks.

'God,' I said, 'look at me, I'm disgusting.' I ran a hand through my tangled hair, 'I haven't washed it in days.'

'Hardly surprising,' Chris said.

'Mum would be appalled. It's a good job she can't see me.'

Chris reached out and stroked the top of my arm.

'Bet you're glad you married me now,' I laughed.

'Every day.'

I rolled my eyes.

'Oh, come on! You're not even a *little* grossed out by me?' I stood up and wiggled my black baggy leggings at him. 'Sexy, no?!'

'Irresistible,' he smiled.

I flopped back down onto the chair next to him and playfully slapped him on the thigh.

'You're ridiculous,' I teased.

'And that's why you love me.'

He pulled me in for another hug.

'You gonna stay and eat something before you go?' I asked, looking up at him.

'No, better if I just head straight back,' he said. 'I can pick something up on the way if I get hungry.'

I broke away and ferreted through my handbag. 'Here,' I

said, placing a small, packaged blueberry muffin into his hand, 'take this.'

He hesitated for a moment.

'I insist,' I said. 'It'll make me feel better.'

We hugged and said our goodbyes. As he walked through the exit door of the hospital and disappeared, I said a silent prayer to myself. 'Keep him safe. Please, please, *please*, keep him safe.'

'How does it look?'

I nodded my head in approval. 'Fab,' I replied, 'it *really* suits you; I knew it would.'

Mum smiled.

'It feels great,' she admitted, swishing her body left and right, and running her hands over the soft material. Her eyes darted to the floor. 'I only wish I could see it properly.'

'Well,' said the nurse, fussing with the neckline, 'you'll just have to take our word for it.'

It really did look good; it fitted perfectly.

'Have you got something we can pop over the top? It's quite cold out.'

I scanned the room. A green angora cardigan was hanging off the back of one of the chairs; Ray had brought it in yesterday. I picked it up and handed it to the nurse.

'Perfect!' She said as she helped Mum into it.

I rummaged through Mum's make-up bag.

'Lippy?'

Mum nodded.

'I'm just going to get your mum's drugs,' said the nurse. 'Back in a sec.'

I knelt in front of Mum and told her to pucker up.

'Don't get any on my teeth,' she warned. 'I don't want to look like Nannie May!'

I smiled at the memory. Nannie May, my paternal grandmother, had always struggled with her sight and towards the end of her life was as good as blind. Despite not being able to see she'd carried on wearing make-up regardless, much, I'm ashamed to say, to our amusement. This consisted of sky-blue eyeshadow, a ton of white powder, blusher and a pale pink lipstick. It was like she'd borrowed a cheap starter kit from a nine-year-old and applied it with much the same level of enthusiasm and inexperience. Forget brushes, Nannie May favoured fingers. If one of us started giggling or ridiculing her efforts Mum would leap to Nannie's defence. 'At least she still bothers with herself; it's good to see she still cares,' she would tell us.

A few minutes later and the nurse was back.

'Here we are,' she announced, placing a bag of drugs on the edge of the bed. 'A nurse from the local palliative care team in Devon will talk you through what they all do and so on tomorrow.'

A wave of nausea swept through me. Palliative care. It hit me afresh: Mum was going to die. My eyes pooled with tears. The nurse discreetly touched the top of my arm in sympathy, then turned to Mum.

'The ambulance will be here shortly,' she said. 'Apparently

you'll be travelling in a brand new one, state of the art!'

'Knock, knock!'

We all looked at the door. It was Doctor Healey – a pretty young woman who had tended to Mum regularly over the last few days. Mum liked her enormously – we all did.

'Hi Sally, it's Dr Healey, I just wanted to come and say goodbye.'

She knelt in front of Mum and took her hands.

'How are you?'

Mum bounced her head from side to side. 'Okay.'

'I should think you'll be glad to get out of here,' Dr Healey said, sweetly. 'And back to the creature comforts of your own home.'

Mum smiled.

'Do you have any questions? Anything you want to talk about?'

Mum looked in my direction.

'I have my family,' she smiled. 'That's all I need.'

'Absolutely,' the doctor agreed.

'Thank you,' Mum said, suddenly. 'You've taken really good care of me. I'm very grateful.'

'It's what we're here for.'

'No,' said Mum. 'Trust me, it's different here – you especially. You'll be an amazing consultant one day.'

Dr Healey blushed and looked genuinely moved.

'And you're a lovely lady. It's been a privilege to care for you.'

This was all getting a bit too much. I turned away.

'It's so unfair that this is happening to you,' Dr Healey continued. 'I desperately wish there was something more we could do.'

'You never know,' Mum replied. 'I might still survive, go into remission on my own with no help.'

A surge of love and pride engulfed me.

'You never know,' said Dr Healey, warmly. 'I'll be keeping everything crossed for you.'

'Sally Jones?'

I spun round. A flush-faced female paramedic was standing in the doorway, panting.

'Yes,' we replied in unison.

'Good,' the paramedic said, rubbing her hands together and smiling sweetly at Mum. 'We've come to collect you and take you home.'

The paramedic was called Sharon; she was the driver. She was accompanied by Nigel – a funny-looking chap with a perfect set of pearly whites. They loaded Mum into the ambulance with minimal fuss and promised to get us back to Devon as quickly as possible. It was a three-hour journey at best. I looked out the window – the wind and rain would slow us down significantly; we'd be lucky if we made it in four. I clocked the time, calculated an ETA and texted Ray.

Nigel had given Mum a powerful sedative before we left the hospital and half an hour into our journey, she was asleep and snoring. Moments later I was thrown forward, the seatbelt nearly cutting me in half.

'Sorry!' said Sharon, gripping the steering wheel. 'This beast is taking some getting used to, it's the first time I've driven it.'

'No problem,' I replied.

'This godawful weather isn't helping,' she chuckled. 'I promise I'll soon get the hang of it.'

Three hours later and we'd arrived at the top of Mum's narrow lane. Sharon looked over her shoulder at me, slightly panicked.

'Down there?'

I nodded.

'Does the lane widen out at all?' Sharon asked, pulling a face.

'Afraid not,' I replied. 'If anything, it gets narrower.'

Sharon's eyes nearly popped out of her head. Nigel spun round to face me.

'There's no other way down?'

I shook my head.

'It'll be fine,' Sharon said cheerily, and playfully slapped Nigel's thigh. 'We promise a door-to-door service and that's exactly what Sally's going to get!'

Mum was rousing. I thought about the ninety-degree turn at the bottom of the lane. I should warn them.

'Holy moly!'

Too late.

'It'll be fine,' Sharon said, ignoring Nigel's concerns. 'Get out and guide me.'

Sharon looked back at me and beamed.

'I love a good challenge!'

I peered out the window. It was going to take a hell of a lot of turns to get round the corner; I wasn't even sure it was possible. Austin Powers and that luggage cart scene sprung to mind.

'Success!' she whooped five minutes later, punching the air with her fist. Her optimism was infectious, and I started clapping.

'Impressive!'

Sharon shrugged.

'Where there's a will there's a way.'

Nigel climbed back into the ambulance.

'Good grief!' Sharon said. 'Look at the state of you!'

Nigel was soaked through and caked in mud.

'The ambulance looks a lot worse,' he said, running a hand through his dripping wet hair. Sharon's face fell.

'Really?'

'Scratch marks all over it,' Nigel nodded.

Sharon gulped.

'It's okay,' he laughed, flashing his pearly whites. 'Like you said, needs must and all that. The panels can easily be replaced.'

'But they've only just been put on!'

'True.'

The two of them stared at each other for a few seconds and then burst into hysterics.

'Where are we?' Mum was awake and attempting to sit up.

I reached out and held her hand, 'Home,' I replied, softly.

Sharon parked the ambulance right outside Mum's house, blocking the entire lane.

'Do you think we should try and get a bit closer?' Nigel asked, looking nervously up and down the lane.

'Nah,' Sharon replied. 'We won't be long and it's hardly the M25 is it?'

They jumped out of the ambulance and opened the back doors.

'Right then, Sally,' Sharon said, smiling, 'let's get you inside.'

Ray and Dad appeared at the front door. I climbed out of the ambulance and gave them both a hug.

'How is she?' Ray asked, lacing her fingers, and blowing air into them.

'Drowsy,' I replied.

'Has she said much?'

I shook my head.

'Slept the whole way.'

Dad stepped out into the rain in his slippers and carried Mum inside.

'Home sweet home,' he said, and gently kissed the top of her head.

'Right,' said Sharon, locking the back doors of the ambulance and wiping the rain from her face. 'We'll be off then.'

I pulled her in for a hug.

'Thank you.'

'No problem, love.'

'Sorry about the state of the ambulance,' I said, reaching out to shake Nigel's hand.

Nigel waved my apology away.

'It's just a bit of mud and a few scratches; your Mum's home and that's all that matters.'

I could have kissed him.

'You're both brilliant!' I gushed. 'Thank you!'

Sharon smiled, climbed into the passenger seat, rolled

down the window and looked at Nigel who was staring back at her, bewildered.

'Your turn!' she said, her eyes dancing with glee.

'S'pose it's only fair,' said Nigel, reluctantly.

Sharon slammed the side of the ambulance with her hand.

'Well come on, don't just stand there! I wanna be back in time for tea!'

'Yeah, yeah,' Nigel looked at me and rolled his eyes. 'Such a bleedin' bossy boots.'

I smiled at him fondly.

'You love her really.'

Nigel considered this for a moment and then nodded. 'All the best,' he said.

'Thank you,' I replied, tears stabbing the backs of my eyes. 'You too.'

I had this ridiculous urge to run after him and beg him to stay.

'Don't leave me,' I whispered as they reversed down the lane and disappeared out of sight. 'Come back and make everything okay.' My feet felt wet. I looked down at them and sighed. I was standing in a massive puddle; my brown suede boots offering zero protection. Good job they were cheap.

'Gus?'

It was Ray.

'Are you coming in?' she asked, her voice full of concern.

Raindrops slid down my nose and splashed onto the ground.

'Come on,' she urged, waving me in. 'You're soaking!'

I looked up at the grey and miserable sky and took a deep breath: it all ends here.

'Just psyching myself up,' I explained.

Ray smiled, reached out her hand to me and pulled me inside.

CHAPTER 20

THE FIRST FEW DAYS

'I'm not taking it off!'

'But you'll freeze!'

'I don't care; I'm going to live and die in it,' Mum sniggered, '*literally!*'

I sighed. This wasn't a fight I was going to win.

'But it's not practical,' I argued.

'I just need a cardy.'

I rolled my eyes and headed for the stairs to retrieve one.

'You know what we should do?'

I stopped on the bottom step and turned around.

'What?' I replied.

'Go through my clothes.'

'All of them?!'

Mum laughed.

'No, silly, just what's in my bedroom. I've loads of knitted dresses that'll really suit you.'

'But you can't see; you won't know what I'm looking at.'

Mum gave me a don't-you-know-me-at-all look.

'I'll know.'

I wavered; it all seemed a little macabre.

'Come on,' Mum insisted. 'We can go through my jewellery too.'

Laura breezed into the room chomping on a banana.

'A nurse from Macmillan will be here in an hour,' Laura said, then froze. 'Mum, what are you doing?'

Mum was trying to hoist herself up. I hurried back to her, bent down and gave her my arm.

'I can do it!' she insisted, waving me away like I was a pesky mosquito.

'We're going upstairs to go through Mum's wardrobe,' I explained.

'You've convinced her to wear something other than the dress you bought her?' Laura said with a smile.

'No,' Mum shot back. 'I have lots of stuff that you *girls* might want. We need to go through it.'

'Ooh,' Laura cooed. 'Sounds fun. I'll get Ray.'

Perhaps it *would* be fun. And it'd certainly help to pass the time.

An hour later and we'd really hit our stride; about a quarter of the contents of Mum's closet was on the floor, ordered into neat little piles. Mum talked us through every item, 'Oooh, I got that at Bluewater. I wore that to the Henley Regatta; crap day – '. She knew the backstory of every garment, where she'd bought it, where she'd worn it. It was astonishing. And Laura was right, it *was* fun! Most of what Mum owned was classic and stylish, but, like all of us she'd fallen for the occasional fad, including a pair of what Mum insisted had once been a very 'on trend' pair of lime and yellow leggings. Ray put them on and strutted around the room; I laughed so hard I gave myself a headache.

'Sounds like you're having way too much fun in here.'

The voice was soft and unfamiliar. A tall man, bald and fortyish, was standing slightly stooped in the doorway, hands stuffed into his trouser pockets.

'Hi,' he said, smiling. 'I'm David, from Macmillan.'

'Hi,' we said in unison.

'Come in, come in,' Laura said, waving him in.

'Mind the mess,' said Ray. 'We're having a bit of a clear-out.'

I removed a pile of clothes from the foot of Mum's bed and offered David a seat.

'Thanks,' he replied, 'but I'm happy standing.'

He walked round to the side of the bed to where Mum was half lying, half sitting.

'You must be Sally.'

Mum nodded.

'Comfortable?'

Another nod.

'Pain?'

'No.'

'Good,' David said, crossing his arms and shifting his weight from one foot to the other.

'Nurses will visit every day to check on you and to administer pain relief.'

'What about all the drugs we were given by the hospital?' Laura asked.

'No one's talked you through them?'

'The hospital said we'd get an explanation from you,' Laura replied.

'Do you have the drugs up here?' David asked.

'They're downstairs, do you want me to go and get them?'

'No, no. We'll go through it all downstairs, before I leave.'

David looked back at Mum and knelt beside her.

'Is there anything you want to ask Sally? Anything you want to talk about?'

His voice was soft and kind of hypnotic. Mum's eyes moistened. It was a while before she spoke.

'Has anyone, you know, in my position ever – '. Mum paused, lowered her eyes, and fiddled with the edge of the duvet, ' – survived?'

David took one of Mum's hands and shook his head.

'Not that I'm aware of.'

Mum smiled.

'Thought not.'

My heart swelled with pain.

'What do you think happens when you die?' she asked suddenly.

David considered his answer.

'Honestly?'

Mum nodded. 'Honestly.'

'I think we live on,' he began. 'Not in our human forms, but in other ways.'

Mum arched an eyebrow.

'How so?' She quizzed.

We all inched in a little closer, keen to hear more.

'Life, in my opinion, is not only physical,' David explained, 'but also cosmic. When the body dies the energy stored within it is released and transforms into something else.'

'Always?'

David nodded.

'Always. Energy is constant; it is never lost.'

Mum smiled.

'So, I'll be around forever?'

'Forever and ever.'

There wasn't a dry eye in the room.

'Of course,' David warned, 'this is just my belief, many would disagree.'

'Well, I like it,' Mum said quietly.

'Me too,' said Ray, blinking away a tear.

'Good,' he said, pulling himself to his feet and smiling.

Did David truly believe what he'd just told us? And did it really matter? It made us all feel better. More importantly, it gave Mum something new to hang on to. The man was a genius.

Lunch was a disaster, a total disaster, and afterwards nothing was ever the same. Cooped up inside for two whole days, we decided to head out for a bit. Mum was in good spirits, so we thought we'd treat ourselves to a spot of lunch at one of Tavistock's most revered restaurants. To start with it all went well but halfway through the main course Mum switched off.

She stared down at her plate of food and started pushing it around with her fork.

'Not hungry,' she said.

Laura thought we should go but Dad wanted dessert; it was part of our meal deal; we were entitled to it.

'Are you okay?' Laura asked for the umpteenth time.

Mum lowered her head and started to cry. Laura shot up out of her chair, walked round to where Mum was sitting and crouched down beside her, 'It's okay,' she soothed, placing a comforting hand on Mum's upper arm, 'we're going.'

Laura and Ray got Mum to her feet and steered her out of the restaurant. Like many of the curious diners surrounding me, I just sat there and stared after them.

'Pud's here!' Dad announced, smiling up at the waiter and pointing at the place mat in front of me. I pushed the bowl away. Dad's brow furrowed, 'Don't you want it?'

Unbelievable. I looked at him in horror.

'What?' he asked, genuinely confused.

I pushed back my chair and stood up. 'We need to go.'

Dad picked up his spoon and scooped up a mouthful of ice cream.

'I'll be with you all in a minute. I've paid for this so I'm going to eat it.'

I wanted to slap him. Instead, I took my coat from the back of my chair, picked up my handbag and walked as quickly as I could away from him.

'There's going to be an official announcement,' I said, excitedly, closing Mum's laptop and pushing it to one side, '*and* an interview!'

'When?' asked Dad.

'Now!' I replied, searching for the remote.

'Got it,' he said, waving it in the air.

'Turn it on!' I demanded, bouncing on my knees, 'quick!'

'What side?'

'BBC1.'

'It won't be long now,' the reporter said. 'We're told the couple will first pose for an official set of photographs and then take questions from Tom Bradby. They have selected him personally as he is someone they both know well and feel comfortable with.'

'Ooooh,' I said, grinning manically, 'we're going to hear Kate speak!'

'What do you think she'll sound like?' Ray said.

'Uber-posh I reckon; she went to Marlborough College.'

'Thought she was a,' Ray chewed her lip, thinking, 'oh, you know, a, um … '

'Commoner?' Dad suggested.

'Yeah! Ray replied. 'A commoner; one of us.'

'There's common and there's common Ray,' Dad said, laughing. 'She didn't grow up in Peckham like your father.'

I let out a little laugh.

'Can you imagine?!'

'Awight?!' said Dad, in his best Peggy Mitchell. 'I'm the future Queen, innit.'

I clasped my hands together and fluttered my lashes channelling my inner Nancy.

'I've dreamt of marryin' me a Prince all my life.'

We all fell about laughing, even Mum.

'And here they come now,' said the reporter. 'Kate resplendent in blue – '

'What? What was that?'

Mum leant forward and squinted at the TV.

'She's wearing blue?'

'Royal blue,' I replied. 'Looks like silk.'

'Cracking legs,' Dad observed.

'The dress is short?' Mum asked.

'Knee length,' I replied, 'fitted at the wai – '

'Shhhh!' Ray cut me off. 'They're about to speak.'

'William,' the reporter began. 'Let's start with you. Where did you propose? When and how? And, Kate, what did you say?

'It was about three weeks ago while we were away in Kenya – '

'Very swish,' said Dad.

'We were away with friends, and I just decided it was the right time.'

'He looks very relaxed, doesn't he?' observed Laura.

'And a bit thin on top,' added Dad. 'Poor lad.'

'We'd been talking about marriage for a while, so it wasn't a massively big surprise. I took her out somewhere nice and proposed.'

'It was very romantic,' said Kate. 'There's a true romantic in there.'

We all looked at each other.

'Posh!' we said in unison and collapsed into another bout of hysterics.

I didn't know it then but the five of us had just shared our last laugh. As the days passed Mum found it harder and harder to join in. She tried, but unless one of us spoke to her directly, she said nothing, preferring to keep whatever it was she was thinking about to herself. It was frustrating, but none of us were prepared to push her. We took it in turns to dress and bathe her and fetch her food; it broke up the monotony. But these little tasks took minutes only; each day was 24-hours long. We filled our time in the usual ways – reading, tidying, watching TV. Ray took Wilf for daily jogs; she said it helped to 'clear her head' and 'keep her sane.'

I desperately wanted to accompany her but dare not leave the house. Mum could have what the nurses called a 'big episode' at any time, and I'd never have forgiven myself if I wasn't around to help calm her down. Laura had an altogether more complicated dilemma. One that, up until a few days prior, I hadn't fully appreciated. Mum had requested another cup of Earl Grey – I don't know why, she'd left the last one and the one before that. Habit, I guess. I walked over to the sink, filled up the kettle and heard a sniff. Laura was sat on one of the high stools by the breakfast bar, staring at the laptop in front of her. It was blank.

'Everything okay?' I asked, plonking the kettle on its base and flicking the switch. Laura shrugged, her eyes brimming with tears. She must have just finished chatting to her family on Skype. I pulled out another stool from underneath the bar and sat down next to her.

'The boys alright?'

'Yes.'

'Mark?'

Laura looked away from me and down at the floor. My insides twisted in panic.

'Is he hurt?!'

'No, no,' Laura sniffed, 'he's just – '

'What?'

Laura blinked away a couple of tears and ran a hand through her hair.

'He's struggling.'

'Struggling?'

Laura nodded.

'He's taking the boys to his Mum's today.'

'That's not unusual, is it?'

'No, but twice in one week?'

'If it helps?'

'Yes, yes, but it makes me feel bad,' Laura blew out her cheeks. 'I've been away for five days, *five* days Kate!' She slumped forward, clutching her head in her hands, 'Seb's only one.'

Tears pricked the back of my eyes.

'But what can I do?' she cried. 'I'm here, I *need* to be here.'

I felt like a total idiot. What did I have to complain about? Yes, being away from Chris was hard but Laura had a whole other family. She had responsibilities and commitments; a life independent from this one. A life that relied on her for its survival. She was its heart, its core, its nucleus. Shame rushed through me; I should've been more aware.

'You know,' I began, 'Mum's not going anywhere just yet. The nurses say she's doing really well. Go home for a day or two; I'll call you if anything changes.'

Laura looked up at me, conflicted.

'Go,' I urged. 'Please.'

'I don't know. What if?'

'Like I said, I'll call you.'

Laura nodded and started drumming the table, weighing it all up.

'The second anything – '

'The very second,' I interrupted. 'Now get your things and *go*!'

'Alright, alright!' Laura smiled, holding her hands up in front of her in mock surrender. 'I'll go, I'll go – you don't have to sound so eager.'

'Well,' I winked. 'You've not been much use to be honest.'

'Hey!'

I stood up and pulled her towards me.

'Give them all a squeeze from me.'

'Will do.'

There were no more words; the hug said it all.

CHAPTER 21

TICK-TOCK, TICK-TOCK

There was something I was beginning to understand about the NHS. If you'd had a test of some kind and it was bad news, you'd get a call within 24 hours; if it wasn't you didn't. The NHS didn't muck about. Serious problems got dealt with without delay. It was reassuring, but terrifying. Mum had had a blood test at ten; the call from the hospital came at four. I answered it in as casual a tone as I could muster.

'We've just got the results of your mum's blood test.'

'Uh-huh.'

'Her white count is zero – '

'What?!'

'Her white count is zero,' the woman repeated.

Everything started to tingle.

'It hasn't climbed?' I asked, nervously, feeling for the wall behind me.

'No, but,' the woman hesitated. 'It's not what you think.'

It wasn't?

'*Everything's* down,' the woman continued. 'Including her HB. It's dangerously low – 3.4.'

My head felt light and fuzzy, like it was stuffed full of feathers.

'She needs a transfusion; without one she'll – '

'Die,' I said coldly, staring straight ahead at the clock flashing steadily on the front of the microwave.

'Yes,' the woman confirmed. 'And soon.'

The clock changed from 16:00 to 16:01.

'*How* soon?'

'A couple of days; it's unlikely she'll make it past the weekend.'

I twitched; today was Friday.

'What do you mean everything is down? And *why* is everything down?'

There was another pause.

'With an HB of 3.4 there really is only one explanation.'

I held my breath.

'Your mum's body is shutting down. The blood transfusion will slow the process down a bit, but – '

' – it won't stop the inevitable.'

'No.'

16:02.

'So, what's the point?'

'The point?'

'Of the transfusion.'

The woman sighed.

'To give you all a bit more time.'

I let out a cruel little laugh. More time? More time for *what* exactly? To observe and endure my mother's demise? No thanks: the woman was insane.

'You don't have to decide right away,' she said kindly, 'but we'd need to know by tomorrow morning at the very latest, preferably before ten so we can order the blood.'

She'd hear from us way before that.

'Of course,' I replied, and quickly hung up.

Transfusion or no transfusion, one thing was certain: Mum's life was all but over; slowly but surely, she was slipping further and further away.

The weekend came and went. Mum refused the transfusion. 'What's it going to give me?' she said. 'A few more weeks? It won't cure me or give me my sight back, will it?'

Laura returned early Saturday morning, re-energised; she took on the bulk of the work while the rest of us sat about and stared into space like zombies. We continued to bring Mum downstairs and sit her by the fire, but the baths had stopped; significantly weaker and relying more and more on oxygen, it just became impossible. Tea was all she requested, but we chucked more than she drank, and by Sunday afternoon the requests all but stopped. *We* didn't though, 'cup of tea Mum?', 'something to eat?' invariably we'd get a slow shake of the head, but occasionally she'd nod, and like racehorses flying out of their starting gates, we were off.

As the day wore on Mum became more and more withdrawn, her big warm eyes blank and distant. I sat myself down on the floor in front of her and stared at her long and hard. 'Let me in', 'tell me what you're thinking.' But my gaze and pleas were ignored. An invisible barrier now existed between us; wherever she was she was out of reach. I searched her face, kissed her hand and turned away.

Later on that night Dad helped Mum upstairs for the very last time. The slow and painful climb up to her room was the last in a series of distressing events starting with mistaking a bowl of grapes for a bowl of soup. She lifted the bowl to her mouth and tipped it. She missed and the majority of the grapes ended up on the floor. She said nothing. This was followed by a failed attempt to get her feet inside her slippers. Frustrated and disorientated she started making indecipherable noises, 'I, I … ah … wha …' She clenched her teeth, grimaced and pointed wildly at her feet, 'Hel, hel, help …' she slurred. I giggled. I *actually* giggled. Dad shot me a 'are you out of your mind?!' look and slipped Mum's feet into her slippers. I caught Ray's eye; she quickly looked away; she too was smiling. What the hell was wrong with us?! Mum stuttered on. 'I ca, can hear … what … not …,' and eventually gave up, slumping forward onto Dad's arms.

'I don't want to be a burden,' she said eventually, as clear as the bright blue sky.

'You're not!' I blurted, keen to make amends.

'I am, I am,' she replied.

'Sshhh,' Dad soothed, stroking the top of her head. 'Let's get you upstairs,' he said, pulling her forcefully to her feet. I winced; did he have to pull so hard?

At the top of the stairs Mum collapsed, banging her head

against the wall. Laura, Ray and I looked on in horror. Mum rubbed her head in confusion while Dad wrenched her back to her feet. She looked like a rag doll.

'I can't feel my hands,' she cried, holding them up and waving them frantically in front of her, 'I can't feel my hands!'

Panic had well and truly set in; she was both visibly and vocally upset. Midazolam. I spun round and faced my sisters.

'Do you think we should give her an anti-anxiety drug, calm her down?'

They looked unsure.

'She's clearly distressed,' I continued.

Laura nodded.

'Which one?' said Ray.

I shrugged and Laura darted into the kitchen. She quickly returned with three bottles and scanned the labels.

'If I remember correctly,' Laura began, inspecting the back of one of the bottles, 'I think Diazepam is the one the nurses said should be used most often as unlike Midazolam it won't completely knock her out.'

Ray and I looked at each other, clueless.

'Girls!' Dad shrieked.

We flew up the stairs in record speed.

'Help me get your mother into bed, she keeps pushing me away.'

Mum was rocking back and forth, her mouth set in an angry line.

'Get off me!' she spat.

Ray rushed to Mum's side.

'Sshhhh,' she soothed. 'It's okay; no one's trying to hurt you.'

Dad reached down towards the bed and threw the duvet to one side.

'Come on,' he said calmly 'bedtime – '

'Stop talking to me like I'm a retard!' Mum snapped.

I looked at Laura. The drug, give her the drug! Laura settled two of the three bottles on Mum's dressing table and quickly removed the lid from the remaining bottle.

'What's that?' Mum snarled, her eyes darting about defensively. Nothing wrong with her hearing then.

'I've got something to give you,' Laura began.

'What?! Why?!'

'It's a pill,' Laura said, calmly. 'It'll help.'

Mum's brow crinkled; she wasn't convinced.

'It really will, Mum,' said Ray, still gripping tightly on Mum's left arm, 'promise.'

Laura picked up a glass of water from the cabinet next to Mum's side of the bed and offered it to her.

'Fine,' Mum said, reluctantly and swiped the glass from Laura's hand.

Five minutes later she was tucked up in bed, quiet and still.

As I stared at the fire it suddenly occurred to me how easy it would be to kneel down in front of it, open the doors, and stick my head inside. I decided to share this thought. The reaction was mixed.

'You what?!' said Dad, muting the TV and staring at me, disbelieving.

Laura and Ray said nothing, but eyed me curiously, like doctors assessing a patient who'd been coaxed down from a bridge after threatening to jump.

'Well, it would, wouldn't it?' I continued. 'The only reason I'm *not* walking over to the fire and sticking my head inside is because I don't want to. But if I did want to, it would be easy.'

Dad scratched his head.

'But why would you *want* to?'

'I *don't* want to. I'm just saying that if I did, it would be easy. Similarly, if I so desired, I could pick up that poker and ram it into your ribs. But I won't because I don't want to.'

Dad took in a long, deep breath.

'Right.'

Unperturbed, I carried on.

'It's only my sound and rational frame of mind that's stopping me, from stopping any of us.'

Laura put down the book she was holding.

'So, essentially, what you're saying is this: none of us in this room would intentionally hurt ourselves, or each other, because unlike the mentally impaired we have absolute control over our actions and decisions.'

'Exactly!' I exclaimed. 'To pick up that poker and shove it up Dad's arse I would have to be completely and utterly out of my mind, depressed say or … incandescent with rage.'

'Why *my* arse?!'

Ray giggled.

'It's just an example, Dad,' I said, rolling my eyes. 'Luckily for you I'm perfectly sane.'

'Yeah,' he replied, sarcastically, 'you sound it.'

I ignored him; I knew he wouldn't get it.

'You may be sane,' said Ray, uncrossing her legs and sitting up tall, 'but you're not yourself, a completely sane person wouldn't even think about such things; I *know* because I've had similar thoughts myself.'

'You want to ram a poker up my butt too?!'

We all laughed.

'No, Dad!' I said, catching my breath. 'Nobody wants to stick *anything* up your big, smelly butt! Keep going on about it though and I might just change my mind.'

Ray was right; I wasn't myself. A darkness had set up home deep, deep within me, and in the months ahead, would come dangerously close to consuming me.

'Kate?' Mum called. 'Is that you?'

'Yes,' I replied.

'What day is it?'

'Wednesday.'

Mum looked disappointed.

'How am I still here?' she mused. 'I keep waiting for something to happen, but – '

Mum sighed and closed her eyes.

'It's ridiculous,' she murmured, and nodded off.

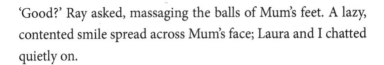

'Good?' Ray asked, massaging the balls of Mum's feet. A lazy, contented smile spread across Mum's face; Laura and I chatted quietly on.

'I'm sorry,' said Laura, her eyes loaded with sympathy.

I snapped my mobile shut and shrugged.

'People have babies,' I said, matter-of-factly. 'It's the way of the world.'

Laura wasn't fooled.

'I know,' she replied softly, 'but I also know it hurts.'

I looked down at my fingers.

'You'll have your baby Kate-kins, you will,' Mum?! Overcome, I edged a little closer to her and squeezed her hand. She squeezed it back and drifted off ...

'I love you,' I whispered and planted a kiss on Mum's forehead; Chanel No 5 ... I slowly inhaled committing the smell to memory.

'Thank you,' she replied, smiling up at me. 'You're a lovely lady and I love you a lot.'

Tears pricked the back of my eyes.

'Ditto.'

I blew out the candle on Mum's dresser, turned off the radio and tiptoed to bed …

I awoke to the sound of rain. It was Thursday; would today be the day? I stretched, yawned, threw on my pink, shabby dressing gown and shuffled sleepily to the bathroom. I grabbed my toothbrush, and lazily brushed my teeth, spluttering toothpaste all over the mirror. Mum wouldn't be impressed; I'd have to clean it. Later, I decided and splashed my face.

How was she still alive? How was it even possible? I didn't want her to die; God, the very thought of it! But she was ready and *had* been for days. There were no more tears; she was done and, admittedly, we were too. I scraped my hair up into a ponytail and headed for Mum's bedroom. I poked my head around the door; she was sleeping. Mozart's *Clarinet Concerto in A* was playing on the radio, Nanna's favourite. I played it for her once, a surprise for her birthday. 'She's been practising for weeks,' Mum proudly informed her, 'I can tell,' Nanna replied, the words catching in her throat. 'It was perfect, Kate, thank you.' I walked over to the radio and turned it up.

I started to panic; there were just two CDs left, and I still hadn't found it. My hands balled into fists, and I let out a scream of frustration. Ray rushed to my side.

'What?!'

'I can't bloody find it, that's what!'

'You're *sure* Mum's got it?'

'I *know* she's got it!'

'And you've checked them all?'

'YES!' I barked. 'Twice!'

'Okay, okay,' Ray backed away a little.

'Sorry,' I hurried. 'It's just really important that I find it; it's one of Mum's favourites.'

'What's it called?' Ray asked. 'I'll see if I can find it on YouTube.'

I slumped back against the piano, defeated.

'I don't know.'

Ray looked confused.

'Then, how do you know what you're looking for?'

I pulled down the cuffs on my jumper.

'I'd hoped I'd recognise the title as soon as I saw it.'

Ray smiled, sympathetically.

'YouTube,' she urged. 'Try YouTube.'

I thought on it for a bit; I needed a moment to recharge. A little while later I picked myself up, stormed into the kitchen and unplugged Mum's laptop.

Two hours later; I was *still* searching. Why was it so goddamned difficult?! They played it all the time on Classic FM. My heart started to thump; of course! I found the station's website, clicked on the 'playlist' tab, and typed 'violin pieces' into the search box. I crossed my fingers and waited for the page to load. I sighed with relief as a long list of titles appeared with accompanying demos. I clicked on the top one and worked my way down. Number eight on the list was by a composer I'd never heard of: Jules Massenet. The piece was called *Meditation*. I hit play. A shiver ran down my spine; I recognised it immediately. Clutching the laptop, I climbed the stairs two by two and sat myself down on the bed beside Mum. I reached over and lightly squeezed her hand. 'I've found it,' I said excitedly. 'Listen.'

'Beautiful,' Mum whispered as soon as it had ended. 'Thank you.'

My face was wet with tears. 'No Mum,' I croaked, 'thank *you*.'

CHAPTER 22

OVER AND OUT

'We can't leave her like that!' Dad barked. 'She'll fall out of bed if we don't move her!'

'I know, but we'll hurt her if we do; she's so frail and confused,' I replied.

'Well, what do you suggest we do then?'

I sighed; Dad was right; we couldn't leave Mum the way she was – half in, half out of bed, but moving her would probably lead to another anxiety attack.

'Kate,' Dad said in earnest, interrupting my thoughts. 'We *have* to!'

Mum heaved herself up and then promptly slid back down; her lips were moving but nothing was coming out.

'Mum?'

Nothing. I tried again.

'Mum? Are you okay? Is there something we can do – get for you?'

Perhaps she needed the loo. I moved the commode a little closer to the bed; we'd moved it into the bedroom a couple of nights ago, so Dad didn't have to struggle with her to the bathroom in the dark.

'Toilet?' I asked.

Mum shook her head but mouthed yes. We got her standing with minimal fuss, but then all hell broke loose.

'Oh no!' Mum cried, hysterically. 'Look! Look! I'm wetting myself!'

Oh God. Mum was panic stricken and trembling.

'It's okay, it's okay,' I said, as calmly as I could.

Dad held her up while I yanked down her pyjama bottoms; they were sodden. Damn it! At that moment Laura and Ray walked into the bedroom. I looked up at them, gratefully.

'Mum's wet herself.'

They quickly set to work; Ray handing me a pantyliner and a clean pair of knickers; Laura stripping the bed.

'Oh, for fuck's sake!' I muttered through gritted teeth.

Ray crouched down next to me.

'You lift her feet,' I instructed. 'And I'll do the rest.'

Together, as always, we fumbled our way through it. But as Dad sat Mum back down on the bed it was clear that something was wrong; something had changed. Mum's eyes were glazed, her face blank. She slumped back onto her pillows and starred up at the ceiling; her mouth ajar and falling to the right. Apart from her chest, which rose and fell with every breath, she was completely still. Where was the resistance? The mouthful of abuse? I looked at the sad and bewildered faces of my family. She'd given in, I knew it and they knew it. Yes, she was still breathing, but the woman she once was had gone.

I'd been awake for ages, listening to the rain; there was a soothing and hypnotic quality to it. I closed my eyes; memories of the night before flooded my brain. Get up and go to her, I said to myself, it might not be as bad as you fear. But what if it was? Worse, what if … no, I would have heard. I glanced at my mobile: nine o'clock.

I heard her before I saw her. The closer I got to Mum's bedroom the louder her breathing became. I peered in; my hand flew to my mouth, the other to my stomach. Mum's eyes were rolled back in her head, the lids flickering and exposing a crescent shaped slither of white. She was breathing through her mouth, her tongue lolling up and down in time with her chest which was rising and falling raggedly and at an alarming rate. A vein in her neck was pulsating, hard. Dad looked up at me, eyes sad and afraid.

'She's been like this all night,' he said, mournfully.

I edged in a little closer.

'Do you think she's in pain?'

Dad shook his head and returned his gaze to Mum.

'This is how is goes. It looks worse than it is.'

I closed my eyes, hiding her from view. Mum wouldn't want us to see her like this. She'd seen her father stiff and lifeless in his coffin and had always regretted it.

'Your sisters are downstairs,' Dad said quietly as if reading my thoughts. 'I'll call you if anything changes.'

I didn't want to leave *or* stay. Dad decided for me.

'Go,' Dad urged, and keeping his eyes fixed squarely on Mum, waved me out of the room.

⊸⊱⊰⊷

The call came just before midday.

'Girls!'

We bolted up the stairs and arrived just in time to witness Mum take two last gasps. The vein that had been throbbing so violently just a few hours ago slowed and stopped.

'If there's a light, darling girl,' Dad whispered into Mum's ear, tears rolling down his face. 'Head towards it.'

He grasped at her hands.

'I love you; I love you.'

We took it turn to say our goodbyes; one final conversation. I sat on the bed beside her and covered her hands with mine. They were soft but cool. I stared at her, drinking her in. She looked beautiful and completely at peace. Tears pooled and fell from my eyes.

'I love you,' I began. 'You'll always, *always* be with me.' I stroked her forehead and carried on. 'I don't know how I'm going to cope without you, I really don't, but I promise I'll continue to make you proud; be the daughter you always believed in.'

Why wasn't she responding?

'Mum?!'

I looked at her eyes willing them to open; then lower, at her mouth imploring her to speak. Why couldn't she hear me?! Why did she look so content to deny me?! I wanted to yell at her, shake her, *force* her to respond. This couldn't be it; there was so much more to say and do. Fat tears streamed down my face and blurred my vision. I wiped them angrily away. I wanted to look at her; keep her with me; imprint her face into my memory. I leaned closer and planted a soft, lingering kiss on her smooth, cool forehead. 'Good luck,' I whispered, as I closed my eyes and breathed her in. 'Stay close.' I stood and walked unsteadily to the door, snatching one last look as I turned to leave.

Laura and Ray were huddled together at the bottom of the stairs looking up at me. I clicked shut the latch on Mum's door and raced gratefully towards them.

The undertakers arrived an hour later. I'd retreated to my bedroom a good half hour before, needing to be alone. Dad led them upstairs and into Mum's bedroom. I heard the familiar squeak of the loose floorboard by Mum's dresser; they were in. And heard the zip of the body bag. I clamped a hand over my mouth holding back vomit. Mum hated confined spaces. I hadn't realised just how much until I saw her gingerly emerge, pale and stunned, from a ride in a light aircraft on her fortieth birthday. It was a gift from Dad. Severely traumatised, Mum spent the rest of the day curled up in a ball on the sofa muttering, 'What on earth was he thinking?' over and over. Dad had simply shrugged, 'I thought it'd be fun.' No complaints this time though. I shook my head, of course not; Mum was dead. Bag her up and toss her to the sharks, she'd be none the wiser. The thought amused me.

'The girls would like her to be dressed in this,' I heard Dad say.

He was referring to the blue dress I'd bought her for her birthday. Mum said she wanted to 'live and die in it' so her wish was our command. A few minutes later, the men were gone.

I glared at them, all of them, one by one, goading them to confront me.

'What?!' I'd bark, if one of them caught my eye. 'Wanna know what's up? My mother died a couple of hours ago and I'm really, *really* fucked off about it! Is that okay? Or have you got something you'd like to say?'

Unnecessary? Yes. Childish? Definitely. Rude? Without question, but man, oh, man the expressions on the faces of those subjected to it – it'd keep me amused for days! This foreign desire to inflict misery on innocent members of the public disturbed me a little, but no need to dwell on it I decided; this was *not* a normal day. Why then were others behaving as though it were? Were they doing it on purpose?! It was raining for fuck's sake! Where on earth had they all come from?! I'd never seen so many people in such a small place – joggers, dog walkers, shoppers: everyday people doing everyday things. It was like they'd conspired to leave their homes at the same time to converge in front of me in some kind of obscene display of supreme health and happiness. Bastards.

'Hi,' said Ray, her bright familiar voice reclaiming my focus.

'Hi,' replied the pharmacist. 'How can I help?'

'Um,' Ray held up a big paper bag, 'I've got a load of drugs here that my Mum was taking. She, er, died today,' Ray stopped, cleared her throat and quickly continued. 'And, um, anyway, one of the nurses who has been looking after her said the drugs that haven't been used need to be disposed of safely and that we should give them to you as you'd know what to do with them. Is, is that okay?'

The pharmacist smiled sympathetically.

'Of course,' she replied. 'No problem.'

'Great!' Ray chirped, as I shoved my fists further into my coat pockets.

'Thanks,' I ventured, and avoiding eye contact, followed Ray out of the store.

Chris called at five o'clock.

'How you doing? he asked, carefully.

I shrugged my shoulders.

'So, so.'

'Are you sure you don't want me to come down?'

'I'm sure,' I replied, flatly. 'You start your new job on Monday.'

'So,' I sighed.

'So, it's not necessary, honestly. I have my sisters. I don't want you tearing down here, having an accident – '

'I won't have an accident.'

'You might.'

'I won't.'

I ran a hand through my hair, exasperated.

'Stay where you are.'

'Alright, alright.'

I sat on the sofa, next to where Mum used to sit, and stared at the empty space.

'I need to tell you something,' Chris said, nervously. 'I was going to wait, but – '

My stomach did a little flip. Chris cleared his throat.

'It's Bamps,' he said quietly. 'He died a couple of hours ago.'

Fresh tears filled my eyes.

'Oh Chris,' I croaked, 'I'm so, so sorry.'

Bamps was Chris' paternal grandfather and one of the loveliest men I had ever met, a true gent. Chris adored him. He had been battling cancer too and in the last few weeks had taken a turn for the worse. He was eighty-two.

'How's your dad?'

'Okay,' Chris replied.

'You know,' I began, stopping briefly and slowly smiling as I allowed my thought to take shape, 'there's something really quite comforting about Mum and Bamps dying on the same day.'

'There is?'

'Yeah,' I replied, wistfully. 'They can look after each other, comfort one another.'

I let out a little laugh.

'They're probably already drunk on G&Ts.'

'If Bamps has made them, for sure.'

'Exactly!' I giggled. 'One-part tonic, two-parts gin!'

Chris' tone turned serious.

'You're absolutely one hundred per cent sure you don't want me to come down?'

'One hundred percent.'

I hung up, switched on Mum's laptop and wrote a heartfelt email of condolence to Chris' dad. Bamps would be sorely missed, I said, and like Mum, impossible to forget.

CHAPTER 23

WHAT NOW?

I wake and remember. An all-to-familiar swell of nausea and fire swirls in the pit of my stomach and with alarming speed and precision finds its way into every part of me. I curl my body together, hugging my knees to my chest in an attempt to slow and control the unstoppable avalanche of pain within me. Hot tears spill from my eyes and soak my cheeks. I scrunch up my face and shake my head in protest, but it's no use; I am under attack and losing. Like a boxer on the brink of defeat, I drop my guard and surrender to a final onslaught of excruciating punches, the fight well and truly over.

'Kate?'

Laura was stood at my bedroom door, her face contorted with grief.

A fresh pang of pain pierces my heart.

'Dad's making scrambled eggs. Interested?' she says quietly, folding her arms into her chest.

Pain stirs in my stomach. I squeeze my eyes and beat my sides willing it to stop.

'Kate?'

Laura sits down next to me and places a comforting hand on the small of my back as I begin to rock back and forth.

'I can't! I can't! I *can't*!' I wail, over and over. 'How can she no longer be here?! 'How?!'

Laura inches closer.

'I don't know,' she replies, positioning herself so that she is now sitting directly across from me, her knees touching mine.

I look up at her, pleading.

'I can't get my head around it. Any of it. To fight so hard and lose so badly.' I wipe my nose on the back of my hand. 'It's unfair,' I sniff. '*So* unfair.'

'It is,' Laura agrees and pulls me in for a hug. I flinch and wriggle out of it.

'I can't,' I explain. 'I just can't …'

Laura smiles.

'It's okay – '

'No!' I interrupt. 'It's not okay. Nothing about *any* of this is okay.'

I turn away; the fire within me raging. 'She's dead, Laura, Mum is dead and there's not a fucking thing I can do about it!'

I didn't mean to shout, and regret it, instantly, but I couldn't help it. If she wasn't here, well then where the bloody hell *was* she? How could she just cease to exist? Mum looks out for me; I look out for her, so what now?

Laura squeezes my hand and stands to leave. She looks as lost and dejected as I feel. I pull the covers up and around me and steel myself for a fresh wave of intolerable pain.

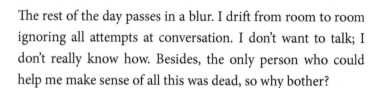

The rest of the day passes in a blur. I drift from room to room ignoring all attempts at conversation. I don't want to talk; I don't really know how. Besides, the only person who could help me make sense of all this was dead, so why bother?

'Kate, c'mon,' Dad pleads the following morning, eyeballing me with concern. 'Come downstairs and eat something. You haven't had anything since ...'

I look up at him, challenging him.

'Since?'

Dad sighs, bows his head and walks away.

A few hours later and I am up and dressed and on my way to the kitchen. But when I reach Mum's bedroom I stop, step inside and inhale long and deep. I scan the room and smile – her little red specs, lens cleaner, oils, a pair of knotted gold studs – it was all still there. *She* was still there. It was like a mini museum, preserving her memory; evidence, *proof* she existed. But I didn't want evidence, I didn't want proof; I wanted *her*. But like the pile of unopened books on her bedside table, I would be forever ignored; forever denied. From now on, if I wanted to see her, I'd have to think about her, remember her.

I started to panic. What if my memory betrays me and I can no longer reach her? My legs give way from under me, and everything goes dark.

By the time I had got myself to the kitchen it was too late for breakfast and too early for lunch. The unmistakable smell of bacon hung in the air, and in the sink, a submerged frying pan. Christian. I knew I needed to eat, but I didn't want to. It was effort, and any sort of effort was beyond me. Effort required a will to do something, and I had zero will to do anything. This, I suddenly realised, was how Laura was able to pack up her stuff yesterday and drive back home. She *wanted* to and it was the 'wanting to' that enabled her to do it. Dad, likewise, was able to watch endless hours of TV, and snack on an inordinate number of nuts, because he wanted to. And Ray, who was conversing and eating with relative ease, had even managed a run with Christian, *presumably* because she wanted to. I could see how it might be possible to do these things if the desire to do them was there, but I couldn't think or feel anything beyond my pain; it was all consuming.

Cereal. I'd attempt cereal. I bent down to the cupboard, removed a box of Special K and poured a small amount into a bowl. I puffed out my cheeks, effort. I reached for the milk, grabbed a spoon, flopped onto one of the bar stools and began forcing it down.

I was still working my way through it when a sweat-drenched Christian limped into the room followed by a gust of arctic wind. I pulled my cardigan around me and shivered.

'Sorry,' he offered. 'It's pretty fresh out there!'

I looked up at him, nodded and spooned in another mouthful. Christian beamed back at me, excited like a kid on Christmas Eve, and rubbed his hands together with glee.

'Your day's about to get a whole lot better!'

Before I could ask him what on *earth* he was on about he had gone and a fantastically familiar figure was walking towards me, arms stretched out in front of him.

I stared at him in disbelief and felt an enormous rush of release. Chris smiled, gathered me up into his arms and gently rocked and stroked me, soaking up all my pain.

'You're here,' I gasped, through broken sobs.

'Of course,' Chris replied, planting a kiss on my forehead.

'But I told you not to …'

'But *I* knew better.'

'But what about work?' I asked, suddenly concerned. 'Tomorrow is your first day.'

Chris shrugged.

'But – '

'But nothing,' Chris interrupted. 'Work can wait.'

I looked up at him, completely overcome. He was wearing his furry Russian hat and the tip of his nose was pink with cold. My God, I loved him.

'Chris!'

Ray, red-faced and muddy, was staring at us from the kitchen doorway, eyes bulging with surprise.

'Gus didn't say you were coming,' she said, wiping her brow and stepping out of her trainers.

'She didn't know,' Chris replied.

'Awwww,' she cooed, and padded towards us. 'Cuddle?'

Chris released me and wrapped his arms around Ray. She sank into him, just like I always did; there were few things more comforting than a bear hug from Chris.

'Wow!' gasped Ray. 'Mum looks incredible!'

Dad picked up the photo Ray was looking at and fondly inspected it.

'Hmmmm,' he mused, smiling at the memory. 'One of my favourites. You know, I was so besotted I enlarged this photo and put it up on my bedroom wall.'

I could see why. If I was a sixteen-year-old boy and *my* girlfriend looked like a raven-haired Aphrodite, I'd pin her up on my wall and stare at her all day too!

'And this one?' Ray, pointed to a photo of Mum in a sunlit garden. She was dressed in a T-shirt and flares and was smiling knowingly at the camera.

Dad's eyes misted over. It was a while before he spoke.

'That was in our garden at Greville Avenue. We'd just found out your mum was pregnant with Laura.' Dad looked at Ray, then me before resting his gaze back on Mum. 'You girls were everything to her; absolutely everything.'

Chris started chuckling and held up a black and white photo

of Dad in a fitted white suit and an open neck shirt.

'Blimey, Tony, Sean Connery's got nothing on you.'

'Very arty,' I observed, suppressing a smile. 'Did the chest hair come with the suit?'

Dad let out a hearty laugh.

'All mine, baby, and your mother loved it.'

'I *bet* she did!' exclaimed Ray. 'You look a bit like Barry Gibb, and Mum *loved* Barry Gibb.'

Chris launched into a surprisingly tuneful rendition of *Stayin' Alive*, his falsetto faultless! Dad sprang to his feet and started to strut. I laughed. I couldn't help myself. It happened without warning. And now I'd started, I couldn't stop. I didn't think I was still capable, but something had shifted, and I was glad of it. Surprised, but glad.

Christian, who'd disappeared for a bit, bounded back into the lounge, eyeing us all with intrigue.

'What did I miss?!' he asked, stifling a yawn and sitting himself on the sofa.

'A bit of Bee Gees magic,' I replied, wiping away tears and gasping for breath.

Ray handed him the photo. Christian's eyebrows hit the ceiling.

'Whoaaa!'

'You're all just jealous,' Dad scoffed, snatching the photo back and admiring it. 'Anyway,' he said looking at Christian. 'You must be feeling a few stone lighter?!'

Christian blushed and wriggled awkwardly on the sofa.

'Yeah …' he began. 'I'd, er, leave it a while.'

Ray shot him a look.

'What?!' Christian cried, holding his hands up in protest, 'I'm a big guy … '

Ray narrowed her eyes and pushed out her chin.

'If the loo is blocked – '

'It's not blocked.'

'It had better bloody well – '

'It's *not* blocked,' Christian insisted. 'Though I have to admit,' he continued, 'even by my standards, it was a bit of a beast.'

Ray wrinkled her nose in disgust.

'Gross.'

I caught Chris' eye and we both smiled.

'A poo of a thousand wipes …'

Ray spun round to look him.

'A poo of a *what* now?'

'A thousand wipes,' repeated Chris. 'It's what you call a poo that requires a never-ending amount of wiping. You've already used up half the bog roll, but somehow you still need more.'

Christian burst out laughing and took a swig of his tequila.

'And,' Chris continued, 'unlike the *perfect* poo, they usually reek.'

'The *perfect* poo?'

Ray cocked her head to one side, intrigued.

Chris nodded.

'It's a thing of beauty.'

'It is?

'Absolutely.'

Chris' eyes were flashing with mischief.

'The perfect poo requires zero wipeage and has the delightful and satisfying scent of a warm biscuit.'

Ray jumped to her feet, clapping wildly.

'You know the ones I mean?!'

'I do! I do!'

We all laughed, and Christian raised his glass.

'To the perfect poo!'

'The perfect poo!'

Dad smiled, shook his head and clinked his glass with mine.

'You're all mad,' he concluded. 'Stark raving mad.'

CHAPTER 24

BYE, BYE, MUM

The page in front of me was blank. I needed more time. I needed patience. Unfortunately, I had neither. Why wouldn't the words come? I glanced at the clock: 11 pm. Fuck. I'd been writing or rather attempting to write Mum's eulogy for well over two hours, and so far, all I had to show for it was crossed out scribble. I knew what I wanted to say, and I was close, but like runaway chickens the words kept slipping from my grasp. I threw down my pen for the umpteenth time and cursed my poor decision to wait until now, the eve of Mum's funeral, to write it.

I could feel myself starting to panic and leapt up from the bed. Perhaps a glass of water would help. I grabbed the empty glass on my bedside table and marched downstairs to the kitchen. I turned the tap and let it run. I tested the temperature – tepid. I smiled knowingly to myself. The water at Laura's house never ran cold. Ever. No matter how long you let it run. It was minus fucking five outside and the water was still tepid. I filled the glass, drained it and slammed it back down beside the sink. Pull yourself together. Stop stalling. Get upstairs and write! I climbed the stairs two at a time and re-entered the room with a renewed sense of purpose. I picked up my pen and frantically started scribbling.

Half an hour later and I still hadn't written anything of any real significance. I balled my hands into fists and started pounding the bed beneath me. I stole a glance at the clock. It was nearly midnight. I bowed my head in defeat and started scripting an imaginary 'sorry I fucked up' speech instead. I then berated myself for giving in and reminded myself to breathe. I looked up searching for inspiration in the starry sky above. One star was notably bigger and shone brighter than all the others. It looked like a diamond. A slow smile worked its way across my face. Bingo. I reclaimed my pen and notepad, uncrossed, and re-crossed my legs, and wrote happily and continually into the early hours.

'Christ, it's cold!' Dad said next to me, his teeth chattering.

'Fucking freezing,' I agreed.

Ray rested her head on my shoulder and hugged my waist.

'At least it's not snowing.'

'True,' I replied and looked to the sky in a silent prayer of thanks.

It had been snowing on and off for days. The weather forecasters had predicted snowfall until the end of the week but as of yesterday afternoon it had first slowed and then stopped altogether.

'Do you think the weather will stop people from coming?' Ray asked, trembling beside me.

'Nah,' said Dad, blowing warm air into his hands before continuing, 'the gritters will have been out all night. It'll be fine.'

I wish they'd gritted Laura's driveway. I looked down at my feet. I was wearing five-inch heels and had very nearly face-planted after skidding slightly and losing my balance. We all had. I let out a little laugh.

'Mum would get a serious kick out of our outfits today.'

Laura giggled and gave a careful little twirl.

'Absolutely!'

Deciding what to wear to Mum's funeral had been a no-brainer. Mum never let a bad weather day get in the way of a good outfit. Unlike the rest of us, who at the first sign of a weather shift would immediately switch into flats and something more practical, Mum would stick to her stilettos. Heels were a fashion staple and would be worn whatever the weather. She owned countless pairs and had sizeable bunions as a result. Still, she looked and felt good, and for Mum, that's what mattered. So today, in her honour, the three of us, despite the arctic conditions, were impractically but stylishly dressed from top to toe. We intended to dazzle, just as she always had.

The funeral director arrived bang on 11.30 am and greeted us all individually. I felt like the Queen. Is this how people would treat me all day? We all climbed into the car, Dad up front in the passenger seat; the three of us, plus Wilf, in the back. Instinctively we grabbed each other's hands and tried to control our breathing. Wilf, who was lying awkwardly over our feet, flopped his head onto Ray's lap and let out a hippo-sized yawn. Mum's last surviving dog was going to walk down the aisle with us to the seats at the front of the congregation. Dogs were a huge part of Mum's life, so including Wilf in this way made total sense. We also hoped it would make people smile. And *that* was our overriding aim of the day. We'd instructed attendees to wear something bright, glam and fun. No black. And as ever, Mum would steal the show, arriving in a bright red, glossy coffin. I couldn't remember whose idea it was, but it was one of the first things we all agreed on. This was Mum's last hurrah, and she was going out with a memorable bang.

We turned into the grounds of the crematorium just a little before midday and rolled to a stop in front of a pair of double doors. Dozens of people, some I recognised, some I didn't, were gathered outside. Fuck. Why weren't they all inside, waiting? I didn't want to see anyone before the service and make polite small talk about the weather. Ray's body tensed and stiffened beside me.

'They're all staring,' she said, almost inaudibly.

'I know,' I replied, squeezing her hand and looking at the sea of faces craning their necks for a better view. 'This must be what it feels like to be a movie star arriving at a premiere.'

'Except there's no red carpet,' said Laura.

'Or Johnny Depp,' I added.

'Imagine!' squealed Laura, licking her lips.

'I am!' I chuckled.

Laura, suddenly serious, looked first at me, then Ray.

'Ready?' she asked.

'Ready,' I replied, giving a few quick nods of my head.

Ray released her hand from my grasp and wiped away a solitary tear.

'Ready.'

We smiled at each other, fuelling each other's resolve, and, one by one, stepped out of the safety of the car, and into the terrifying and expanding horde outside.

I scanned the crowd and quickly found him. Chris was standing and chatting with half a dozen or so of my school mates. I broke away from my sisters and walked over to them.

'Jones,' said Lori, her big brown Bambi eyes wide as saucers. 'You look amazing!'

I patted my beehive and smoothed down my dress.

'Why thank you,' I drooled. 'Impractical, expensive – a fitting tribute.'

Rosalie smiled and reached for my hand.

'You've eaten?'

I rolled my eyes, affectionately. Rosalie was a nurse and one of the most sincere and compassionate people I knew.

'Porridge *and* eggs,' I boasted. 'But I think I might be regretting that a bit now.' I said clutching at my stomach for effect.

Someone patted me on my shoulder. It was my dad's cousin. She pulled me in for an embrace, nodded and left. In her place came a tall, middle-aged woman wearing tweed.

'Hi Sue,' I smiled. 'Thank you for coming.'

'Of course!' She replied. Eager to leave, I looked and smiled at the familiar female face behind her, but Sue reached out and blocked my path.

'You've certainly changed,' she said, sweeping her eyes up and down my body and across my face approvingly.

I wasn't sure if I should thank her or punch her. Sue's lack of tact was legendary. Mum had taken a lifelong dislike to her after she'd found out from a trusted family friend that she'd disapproved of her son's growing interest in Ray and had discouraged him from pursuing her. 'How dare she?' Mum would rant, eyes blazing with rage. 'Bloody cheek! He'd be lucky to have her!' Perhaps I should ask her outright if she still held this view?

'Thank you,' I smiled, deciding to play nice, and quickly made my escape.

Two men in top hats opened the doors to a spacious room and ushered everyone inside. Laura, me and Ray hung back and regrouped by the car. I was about to fill them in on my awkward exchange with Sue when Ray let out a heartfelt gasp. I turned around and froze. Mum. A swarm of butterflies took flight inside me, and a fierce lump lodged itself firmly in my throat. Keep it together, I pleaded silently to myself. Keep it to-fucking-gether. I reached for my sisters and silently wept as Dad and my uncles carefully unloaded Mum from the hearse and hoisted her onto their shoulders. Tears exploded from my eyes and my body started to shake. Ray rubbed the top of my arm and kissed the side of my face; a full-on breakdown wasn't an option. I looked away and tried to focus on my breathing, but it was quick and ragged; impossible to latch onto. We took up our positions behind Mum and started walking, Wilf wedging his head between my leg and Ray's and keeping it there until we'd reached the seats reserved for us at the front of the congregation.

Sitting, facing no one, and with my back to over one hundred people was deeply unnerving. I could feel the eyes of the entire room boring into the back of my head.

'We are here today,' the celebrant began. 'To celebrate and honour the life of Sally. A doting mother and much-loved wife and sister.'

I tried to listen, but I was too jittery. I bowed my head and fixed my gaze on a fuzzy orange stain on the concrete floor.

'A few words now from Sally's daughters …'

Daughters? Shit. That was me. I had to get up. I had to get up and face the room. What if I couldn't do it? My legs turned to jelly. Laura reached for my hand, helped me to my feet and led us to a small platform at the front of the congregation, stopping just to the left of centre, so that we could all fit comfortably on. Dad, who had sat himself on the row next to us, smiled and nodded encouragingly. Laura opened her mouth to speak but nothing came out. I instinctively moved my hand behind her and rested it on the small of her back. Laura closed her eyes, swallowed hard and tried again. I zoned in on my heartbeat. It was beating fast and by the time Laura had finished, single beats were indecipherable. I placed my hand on my chest and reached into the pocket of my dress with the other, carefully removing a folded piece of paper. Ray handed me a tissue and as I dabbed at my eyes the words imprinted on it sprung clearly into view.

'Mum was a diamond,' I began, a little croaky but audible. 'A cut above the rest.' I looked up, took a moment to breathe and carried on.

All eyes and ears passed to Ray. She got through the first bit, but faltered soon after, her voice breaking and fading. I pulled her in close and slowly and carefully read the last of her words out loud …

By five o'clock I was well and truly pickled and bear-hugging anyone within touching distance. I was in an alcohol-fuelled love haze and it felt good. *Really* good.

I looked at my champagne flute: empty. I made my way to the bar, tripping over chair legs and spotted my uncle, who by the look of it was as drunk as I was.

'That's my girl,' he slurred, wrapping his giant frame around me. 'Back for another.'

I released myself from his embrace and patted his protruding stomach with affection.

'Too bloody right!'

He nodded in approval.

'What'll it be?'

I slammed my glass onto the counter and slid it towards the fizz.

'Flubbles,' I replied.

'*Flubbles?*' He repeated, looking a little unsure.

I dissolved into a fit of giggles.

'Bubbles,' I managed eventually. 'I meant bubbles!'

My uncle roared with laughter, picked up the bottle and poured.

'Flubbles it is!'

I drained my glass, refilled it and looked around the room. It was buzzing. Mum was very much the centre of attention, just how we'd hoped she would be. Supersized prints adorned the walls and songs – Mum's lifelong favourites – blared out from the speakers. This wasn't a sad occasion; it was a party; a party befitting its life-loving host. But by six o'clock the room was thinning and my heart sank. I didn't want it to be over. Over had come way too soon.

Laura handed me a bin bag and showered my face with kisses.

'Just chuck it all in,' she instructed. 'I'm gonna make a start clearing and stacking the chairs.'

I nodded reluctantly and fell to the floor. Chris looked over from the hall doorway, concerned. Sober, he was taking people to the train station, and by the look of the length of the line forming it was gonna take a while. I mouthed, 'I'm fine,' and waved him on his way.

An hour or so later only a handful of us were left. Just one more stuffed bin bag to add to the heap in the skip outside and we'd be on our way. I picked it up, slung it over my shoulder and as I started to walk towards the door Christian flew past me, landing with an almighty thud on the stone-cold concrete floor in front of me.

He wasn't moving. I dropped to my knees beside him.

'Christian?!'

Nothing. I tried again. A little moan escaped from his mouth. He pushed himself up, rubbing his head. Ray rushed over to us.

'Christian?!' She roared, eyes blazing. 'What the hell was that?!'

Christian responded with an inaudible muffle.

'So stupid!' she muttered and hauled him to his feet.

Christian clamped one hand over his stomach and the other over his mouth and darted out the door, Ray in hot pursuit. Dad unplugged Mum's iPod and walked over to me.

'He's drunk a whole bottle of Jack Daniel's, apparently.'

'Well, that'll do it,' I replied, laughing a little.

'Do what?' Dad asked, puzzled.

'Convince you, you can fly!'

Dad reached up and removed the final photo of Mum from the wall. He looked at it and then cast his eyes around the room, quiet and bare once more.

'It went well, didn't it?'

I felt a surge of pride.

'It did,' I nodded. 'It really, *really* did.'

CHAPTER 25

MOVING ON

I took a massive swig of my wine and hit mute on the remote. Jools Holland was yabbering away about some godawful band on his equally godawful *Hootenanny*. The show was beyond depressing. Everything about it was a slap in the face; a glaring reminder that unlike Jools and his merry throng of insipid musicians, you were alone, unwanted and insignificant; someone who for whatever reason, didn't feel they really had any other choice but to tune in. 'Happy New Year, Kate,' I said quietly to myself and wandered over to the window.

Christmas had been and gone but the outside of our block of flats was still lit up like a casino. On the driveway by the doorway of the house opposite a giant inflatable Homer Simpson was bobbing about in the breeze. He was dressed like Santa Claus. I imagined walking over there and stabbing his big, bulging eyes with a kitchen knife. And saw myself smiling as I watched him deflate. I quickly looked away and hit my head with the heel of my hand. Thoughts such as these were happening more and more and I was finding it increasingly difficult to stop them. I was at the mercy of something dark and beastly that lurked deep within me. It clawed at me, incessantly, willing me to respond. And like a junkie craving a hit, it had become almost impossible to resist.

I took another swig of wine. It just wasn't fair, any of it. What if life for me had already been as good as it was going to get? What if I was now stuck in some perpetual cycle of misfortune? Maybe this moment of misery would become my new normal. Maybe I deserved it. I sighed and flopped back down on the bed. What was it my counsellor said? Something about the way I felt was to be expected and *not* reacting to it all would be a way bigger worry. We can only take so much, he said, and when the load gets too heavy, like a soggy, waterlogged ceiling, we collapse and crumble into messy heaps on the floor. The hopes and crushing disappointments of the last two years had taken their toll; my brain and body had had enough. I felt everything and nothing *all* the time. I ignored it until I no longer could. Until I broke our bathroom mirror into a million little pieces.

It happened on the previous Friday, two weeks after I'd arrived at my new home in Derby. My days were empty and meaningless. Chris was at work and everyone I knew and loved lived hundreds of miles away. I would sit on the sofa, switch on the TV and wait. And while I waited a slide show of depressing images of a future I would never know would spin round and around in my mind, tormenting me on and off for the rest of the day. On my better days though, days like the day I broke our bathroom mirror, I sought a more productive distraction and tried to actually *do* something.

Chris was one hundred per cent on board with my decision

to paint the frame and bought everything I needed the day before from a local DIY shop on his way back from work.

'It'll look amazing!' he said brightly the following morning while munching on a piece of toast. 'Brand new! I can't wait to get home and see the end result!'

Keen to match Chris' enthusiasm I set to work, and by midday, instead of reaching for a bottle of wine, I grabbed my phone, called Chris and gushed on and on about what an incredible job I'd done.

It'd look even more impressive back up on the wall, I decided a few hours later, and carefully picked it up from off the floor and walked to the bathroom. But as I lifted it high above me and reached for the hooks on the wall, the mirror slipped from my grasp and crashed to the floor, shattering, like me, into a million tiny pieces.

Chris came home just after five and found me still sitting amongst all the broken glass.

'Kate?!' he cried and crouched down beside me. 'Are you hurt? What happened?'

I didn't respond. I couldn't. I was doomed. I was cursed. Nothing was ever going to go my way again. I was to be robbed of happiness and normality for the rest of my life.

Chris disappeared and returned with a dustpan and brush and started sweeping up the debris around me. I said nothing.

'What happened?' Chris asked again putting down the dustpan and brush and lifting my chin with his forefinger. And as our eyes met a tsunami of words exploded from my mouth.

'Seven years bad luck! Seven *fucking* years! This shit show of a year was just the beginning. I, and you, if you choose to stay with me, are destined to be eternally unhappy. Everyone else in the world will continue to spawn with repetitive ease and you and I will be cast aside and forgotten. People who once liked us and enjoyed spending time with us will stop inviting us to things and we'll wind up sad, alone and pitied. "Remember Chris and Kate," they'll say wistfully, while tucking into their Sunday roasts and gazing adoringly at their freckled-faced offspring, "such a nice couple. It really is a shame how things turned out for them.'"

Chris' brow furrowed slightly then instantly softened. He cupped my face in his hands and leaned towards me until his forehead was touching mine.

'Kate,' he said slowly and deliberately, stroking my cheeks with his thumbs. 'I think you need to talk to someone …'

He was right. I did need to talk to someone. Offloading my fears to a complete stranger and admitting I was struggling, was a huge relief. I wasn't going mad. I wasn't weak. I was battle-weary. And in time, the wounds inflicted on me would heal and the pain would ease. I was still me, apparently. He even said I would eventually emerge improved, but only if I acknowledged my pain and stopped pretending it wasn't there. 'Let it rise,' he advised. 'Feel it.'

I was feeling it alright, every hour of every goddamned day. It was hard to see how allowing myself to wallow in it would serve me, but life had already surprised me countless times and in numerous ways so I was open to the idea that it could.

———⟨⟨⟨⟩⟩⟩———

Clutching a bottle of prosecco and a tray of hot savoury treats, Chris pushed open the doorway to our bedroom with his foot.

'Refills!' he announced and walked carefully towards me.

'Ooo goody,' I said, pushing myself up from my elbows and holding out my empty glass. Chris filled it and jumped onto the bed beside me.

'Sick of Jools, already?' he asked, pointing at the silent TV in front of us.

'Yep,' I replied, leaning over him and taking a miniature Yorkshire pudding. 'I couldn't endure another minute.'

'Fair enough,' he said washing down his food with a generous glug of prosecco. 'Death by Jools Holland would be a pretty lame way to go.' And picking up the remote, he started flicking through the channels. 'Let's find something else.'

A rush of love and gratitude surged through me, like it so often did when Chris was around. He always knew what to say and do to make me feel better. I drained my glass and snuggled into him. I may not be where I thought I would be but lying here in the arms of the man I loved I was exactly where I *wanted* to be. Love made everything okay. Its capacity to push us on, revive us and open our eyes to the seemingly impossible was nothing short of miraculous. I had absolutely no idea where I was headed, but in all honesty, who does? I pulled Chris in a little tighter, moulding myself around him. My safety. My constant. Home.

EPILOGUE

Mum surveys her handiwork, whips off one of her gloves and wipes her forehead with the back of her hand. She turns to face me, smug and satisfied. I lightly clap. The lawn looks immaculate. I start to walk towards her. But as I pick up speed, and inch closer, Mum starts to fade. 'No!' I hear myself scream and break into a run, but my feet give way from under me, and I fall to the ground in a twisted heap. Mum reaches both arms out towards me. I pick myself up and break into a run.

'I'm coming,' I say quietly. 'I'm coming.'

I zone in on her face, pick up speed and will myself on. The gap was finally closing, and Mum was getting closer. I fling my arms out in front of me; just a few more steps. Mum beams and wraps her arms around me like a giant bow. I bury my face in her soft, curly hair and squash out all the air between us. 'I miss you,' I sob. 'Every second of every day.'

'Oh darling,' she replies, clear as a bell. 'I miss you more, so much more.'

But before I can protest, she is gone.

I puffed out my cheeks and stroked my belly. Like every memory of Mum, it was bittersweet. It all felt so real. But every dream felt real these days, a strange side effect of pregnancy. It was so good to see her again, but heart wrenching to wake from.

I looked down at my expanding bump and smiled. Three months to go. The journey, as expected, had been far from easy, but none of that mattered now. I circled my belly button and caught a glimpse of my mum's gold ring. How happy she'd be. How proud she'd be.

I felt a nudge from within and let out a little giggle.

'Alright, alright.'

I scanned the table and located my diary. This next bit was gonna be tricky and I had a deadline. A self-imposed deadline, but a deadline, nevertheless. I'd make it though. Writing about Mum was the perfect distraction from all my 'will-I-make-it-to-full-term' pregnancy fears. It also kept her close, and I needed her.

I took another sip of water, picked up my diary and leafed through the pages until I found it.

'Nothing is ever lost to us as long as we remember it.'

Today, tomorrow, forever.

Mum was going nowhere.

END